WRITERS 750 EMERALD WORKBOOK

Professor Limn Books
Charlotte, NC

Giant Tales 3-Minute Stories

Beyond the Mystic Doors

From the Misty Swamp

World of Pirates

Dangerous Days

Giant Tales 10-Minute Stories

Lava Storm In the Neighborhood

Final Ships In the Neighborhood

WRITERS 750 EMERALD WORKBOOK

A Writer's Workbook for

DEVELOPING STORIES

Explore New Conflicts and Write Monthly Stories

H. M. SCHULDT

Professor Limn Books
Charlotte, NC

Writers 750 Emerald Workbook:
A Writer's Workbook for Developing Stories

ISBN-13: 978-0-9885784-9-4
First published in 2020 by Professor Limn Books

Printed in the United States of America 2020

DEDICATED TO

SERIOUS WRITERS

ASPIRING WRITERS

NEW WRITERS

RETURNING WRITERS

FICTION WRITERS

&

SEASONED WRITERS

ABOUT THE AUTHOR

Heather Marie Schuldt
is a leader in the creative writing community.
She offers a monthly short story contest
in a writing group that she founded in 2012,
Writers 750.
She compiled many of the best 750-1,000 word count stories
in a collection of anthologies called *Giant Tales 3-Minute Stories.*
She compiled many of the best 2,500 word count stories
in a collection of anthologies called *Giant Tales 10-Minute Stories.*
Heather is an author and professor
who reaches into the
heart and soul of each reader
by working with topics,
themes, settings, and highlights.

She encourages authors to draw upon
their skill and talent,
bringing forth a new and
wonderful piece of work in the
craft of writing fiction.
Although this book is intended
mostly for experienced authors,
it is also for new and returning writers
who are looking to craft an original tale.

Heather is a wife, mom to three,
apologist, and an advocate
for writers to write in such a way that
honors the two greatest commandments.
She earned a Master's Degree in Religion
from Southern Evangelical Seminary, and
she lives in North Carolina
with her family and English Bulldog.

HOW TO USE THIS WORKBOOK

Writers 750 Emerald Workbook:
A Writer's Workbook for Developing Stories
is a workbook for writers to write a new story every month for twelve months.

WHAT WILL I DO?

The basic goal is for you to write one new short story each month for twelve months. You are in charge of whether you want to write more or less. The suggested word count for your story each month is in the range of 750-1,500 words, which makes your story a minimum of 3-minutes long. If led to do so, you are welcome to extend your story into a 10-minute story or even into a novella or full-length novel. Writers who are in a writer's group, a book club, or a Bible study group will be able to share a new story with the group. You will have the opportunity to develop writing skills and use your talent to exercise the craft of writing a good story.

WHAT WILL I LEARN?

You will be introduced to several topics and underlying themes. Each month, you will be given several different suggestions for story options to write about. You will explore new settings and concepts. As a writer, you will learn perseverance and become more knowledgeable about writing a good story. You will be given many tools to write a new story each month. By writing a story each month, you will have the opportunity to compile your stories into an anthology. You will also practice giving pitches for writing conferences.

DIRECTIONS FOR EACH MONTH

1.) At the beginning of the chapter, read the theme, setting, and highlights for the month. In the "Resources for You to Explore" section each month, you will find short stories, personal testimonies, fiction, non-fiction and/or poems.
2.) Read through "Optional Conflicts" and circle any that might interest you.
3.) Work through the rest of the chapter to discover the story that is sitting in you. Write your story. Print it out and write your pitch at the top of the "Pitch Page" each month. Fold it in half and place it at the end of the chapter. At the end of twelve months, you will have twelve short stories.

WHAT KIND OF WRITER AM I?

Many different kinds of people can use this workbook. You can use this workbook as an independent writer, a writer in a group, a book club writer, an anthology writer, or a novelist writer. Decide which one works best for you. If you are not sure, then be an independent writer for now. You might even realize you fit into a few areas at the same time. You might even fit very well into all five areas. Which one or more of these categories do you hope to fit into?

1. **INDEPENDENT WRITER** – The independent writer will work on his or her own. This kind of writer is determined, motivated, interested, and committed to writing stories. When given a new theme and setting each month, the independent writer is ready for a new challenge. The independent writer will use this workbook each month to explore new themes and new characters, working around his or her schedule.

2. **GROUP WRITER & BOOK CLUBS** – The group writer might be online or in person. The group writer is motivated to write a new story while sharing it in a group for the purpose of getting an award, winning a contest, or simply reaching out to neighbors. The group could focus on giving awards instead of determining winning stories or they can do both. The group should have a leader to help give a new theme each month, manage voting, hand out awards, or just provide cheese and wine. Visit Writers 750 Program online to connect with a group.

3. **BIBLE STUDY GROUP WRITER** – The Bible study group writer will use this workbook for writers, readers, and fellowship. Writers are welcome to write a new story each month, but not everyone in the group is required to write stories. The group leader can follow suggestions for the group writer, but other people who are not writers are welcome to participate. As with any Bible study group, the purpose is to draw people closer to the Word of God and lift up His name. Read 1 Corinthians 10:23-33. *Do all to the glory of God.*

4. **ANTHOLOGY WRITER** – The writer who wants to collect many short stories and compile them into one book, an anthology, can use this workbook to publish stories with a common theme or a collection of themes. The *Giant Tales* anthologies include over fifty authors from Writers 750 who submitted a short story each month.

5. **NOVELIST WRITER** – The writer who begins writing a new story might find that he or she wants to write a longer story, more than just a 3-minute story or a

10-minute story. This kind of writer is welcome to use this workbook to write a novella or a full-length novel.

Introduction

Writers 750 Emerald Workbook came into existence after years of hard work. I have to give a big thank you to each and every writer who knows the value of developing a good story. It is humbling to know many talented writers who enjoy writing a good story. For certain, writers can bring about a masterpiece if given a little bit of encouragement. I decided to offer a workbook where writers can find a specific opportunity to give hope for a better future, offer healing to those who are hurting, and give encouragement to endure difficult times. As a light shining in dark places, writers can make a significant impact for the better. We are all in this life together, searching for good stories, needing to do what is right and good. I believe a good story should include a meaningful lesson - without necessarily sounding instructional – even if it happens to be entertaining. Like many other people, I enjoy reading short stories!

This workbook has been designed to let the writer - in you - consider a number of topics, settings, conflicts, and themes that will inspire the writer to tell a meaningful tale. Whether the story is a tragedy, a cliffhanger, adventurous, or heroic, each writer will have the freedom to develop a new story each month and do his or her very best to complete the story as if the story were being read out loud to an audience.

The format of this workbook has been designed to help the writer each month for twelve months. You can start at any time during the year. Each of the first eight months of this workbook directly relates to a certain chapter from *Giant Tales Beyond the Mystic Doors* or *Giant Tales From the Misty Swamp.* Whether you want to read what other authors have written is entirely up to you. Thank you for taking on the task of writing a good story. Life is an adventure! Writing stories just might be the biggest adventure of all.

HEATHER MARIE SCHULDT

TABLE OF CONTENTS

SEASON ONE

MONTH ONE: Doorway to a Better Place

MONTH TWO: Outsmart the Villain

MONTH THREE: Appointments

SEASON TWO

MONTH FOUR: Disturbing Conflicts

MONTH FIVE: Misty Swamp

MONTH SIX: Unusual Weather

SEASON THREE

MONTH SEVEN: Carnivals

MONTH EIGHT: Masks

MONTH NINE: Heirlooms

SEASON FOUR

MONTH TEN: Tricksters

MONTH ELEVEN: Noises

MONTH TWELVE: Emerald City

MOTIVATION TEST

WHY DO YOU WANT TO WRITE A SHORT STORY?

DIRECTIONS: Bubble in all of the following reasons why you would like to write twelve new short stories. On the line provided, rate yourself on a scale from 1-5. Give yourself a 1 if it is a low amount. Give yourself a 5 if it is a high amount. Once you are finished, read the *Scoring Section* and *Results Section* on the next page. Take this test again in one year when you finish this workbook to find out how much your motivation has increased.

The reason why I am writing a new story is because…

o 1 _____ I am a writer, and that's what I do - write!
o 2 _____ I want to make the world a better place.
o 3 _____ I want to help someone change their life for the better.
o 4 _____ I need to pound out a new story full steam ahead.

o 5 _____ I feel better when I am writing and when I finish a story.
o 6 _____ Writing is my central focus of work to help other people.
o 7 _____ My career is in writing or I want my career to be in writing.
o 8 _____ Writing is a productive hobby of mine or I am an aspiring writer.

o 9 _____ I am compiling stories or I want to compile short stories into an anthology because I want to help other people.
o 10 _____ I need to stop worrying about grammar guidelines – and just write a new story!
o 11 _____ I become a better writer when I am learning new skills.
o 12 _____ It is an honor to let my story bless my neighbor.

o 13 _____ I finished another story, and I need to keep writing new stories.
o 14 _____ I need to write a short story so I can get back to my other writing project.
o 15 _____ Writing a story is like cooking a pot of soup. I need to keep all the burners going to feed a flock!
o 16 _____ Writing is my primary gift from the Holy Spirit.

o 17 _____ I need to get another story out on paper.
o 18 _____ I have a story inside that I need to tell.
o 19 _____ I need an excuse to invite people over.
o 20 _____ I keep thinking about what my readers need to hear.

SCORING SECTION

Once you finish bubbling in all that applies to you and you rate yourself on a scale from 1-5, please use the following two different sections for scoring:

SECTION ONE
Give yourself 1-5 points for each of the following numbers:
1_____, 4_____, 5_____, 8_____, 10_____
11_____, 13_____, 14_____, 17_____, 18_____

SECTION TWO
Give yourself 1-5 points for each of the following numbers:
2_____, 3_____, 6_____, 7_____, 9_____
12_____, 15_____, 16_____, 19_____, 20_____

Add your numbers in Section One to get a Section One total: _________

Add your numbers in Section Two to get a Section Two total: _________

Find your results on the next page.

RESULTS SECTION

SECTION ONE – This section refers to the level of awareness you may or may not have regarding the need to write short stories. The purpose of this section is to help you become more aware of the writer in you and to encourage you to use your writing gifts each month by developing a new short story.

Score 0-10 — As a beginner, you should consider taking it one month at a time with the goal of reading the chapter without any pressure to write a story. Feel free to write a story if you want to.

Score 11-30 — You have enough awareness to know that you should be using your writing gifts to write a good story. Make it your goal to write a 750-word count story each month. Take it easy on yourself if you skip a month.

Score 31-40 — At this level, you most likely know that writing is probably your main gift or at least one of your gifts in the area of communication. Your monthly goal should always be to finish one story with a minimum word count of 750 words.

Score 41-50 — This high level shows that writing is most likely your primary gift. Your goal will be to finish each month with at least one new story of a minimum of 750 words while handling multiple writing projects at the same time.

SECTION TWO This section refers to the level of awareness you may or may not have regarding the need to write a short story for the benefit of edifying others. The purpose of this section is to help you become more aware of using your writing gifts and skills for the benefit of others.

Score 0-10	You might be new to building up one another. Try to read each chapter and see if you can find a way to use your writing skills to help one another. Begin to ask for feedback and listen carefully to any suggestions.
Score 11-30	You have enough awareness to know that your writing gifts can benefit other people. Make it a goal to write in such a way to lift someone up, encourage someone, or help them in some way. Ask readers for feedback and make any adjustments you need to make. Consider leading a group of writers or hosting a writing group in your community or home.
Score 31-40	At this level, you most likely know that your writing has already been benefiting other people. Your monthly goal should be to make sure that your stories are edited. Make your stories available to others by way of a blog or other publications. Get into a group setting with readers, editors, and other writers. Consider publishing your writing in an ebook and in print.
Score 41-50	This high level shows that you have already been writing for the benefit of others. Your monthly goal should be to make sure your stories are edited and get them in front of readers by way of a blog and in a group setting. Make sure your writing is honoring to the Creator of the universe. In addition, consider if your writing could be made available in a published ebook as well as in print. Practice your pitch, attend a writer's conference, and find a good publisher.

In one year, when you finish writing twelve new short stories, take this test again. The purpose of this test is to see your progress after one year.

Whether you eat or drink, or whatever you do, do all to the glory of God. – 2 Cor. 10:31

SEASON ONE TOPICS FOR

MONTHS 1, 2, & 3

Month One: DOORS

Month Two: VILLAINS

Month Three: APPOINTMENTS

OUTLINE FOR SEASON ONE: MONTHS 1, 2, & 3 TOPICS

I. Month One Topic: Doors

   A. Optional Conflicts
   B. Settings
   C. Traveling with Courage
   D. Write What You Know
   E. Pitch

II. Month Two Topic: Outsmart the Villain

   A. Optional Conflicts
   B. Favorite Stories, Heroes and Villains
   C. Write What You Know
   D. Identify a Greedy Villain
   E. Explore an Escape Plot
   F. Pitch

III. Month Three Topic: Appointments

   A. Optional Conflicts
   B. Memorable Appointments
   C. Grabbing the Reader's Attention: Hooks
   D. Pitch

MONTH ONE TOPIC:

____

DOORS

Welcome to *Month One!* Let's begin!

If you have not already read *How To Use This Workbook* located at the beginning of this workbook, please do so now. Write the current month and year on the line above.

WHAT WILL WE DO IN THIS CHAPTER?

Below, you will find an outline showing that we will be covering the following items: optional conflicts, settings, traveling with courage, write what you know, and pitches. You can find an outline at the beginning of each season.

Each month, at the beginning of each chapter, you will see a new theme, new setting, and new optional conflicts. They are meant for you to explore in order to get started on writing a new story. In this chapter, we will examine the nature of developing a good setting and traveling with courage. We will also learn different ways for you to find a good story that is waiting in you. We will introduce what it means to "write what you know."

Month One: Doors

A. Optional Conflicts
B. Settings
C. Traveling with Courage
D. Write What You Know
E. Pitch

MONTH ONE DIRECTIONS

The following directions will stay the same for each month. A condensed version will be given to you at the beginning of each month to focus back on writing.

1. Read the theme, setting, and three highlights in order to begin thinking about what kind of story you want to write. Challenge yourself to include three suggested highlights in your story.
2. Read through the next section, "Optional Conflicts to Get Your Started." Read through the rest of "Month One" and circle any story ideas you might want to explore. Every month will end with "Write What You Know" and "Pitch."
3. Begin writing your new short story! When you complete writing your new story, print it out, write the pitch at the top of the page, fold it in half, and place it at the end of the chapter in this workbook. In one year, you will have twelve stories! (Note: If you read this entire workbook without writing any short story at all, the entire point of the workbook has been missed. The main goal of this workbook is for you to write at least one short story each month for twelve months.)

THEME OF COURAGE

THEME: Courage – Doorway to a Better Place

SETTING: Your character is about to face a difficult situation beyond his or her control. You decide if the sky is falling, if he or she lost a job, if the current job requires a dangerous task, or if something destructive has become an obsession that needs to go. As with any door, you describe how things are different on the other side. Describe how your character needs to use courage to get through the struggle.

3 HIGHLIGHTS (Challenge yourself to include these three highlights): A door, a struggle, and a lesson learned

WORD COUNT: 750-1,500

DEADLINE: 25th of the month

RESOURCES FOR YOU TO EXPLORE:

- *Giant Tales Beyond the Mystic Doors,* Chapter 1: Mystic Doors
- *Book of Courage* by John T. Faris
- *Captains Courageous* by Rudyard Kipling

OPTIONAL CONFLICTS TO GET YOU STARTED

1. Your character finds a secret door that leads to a certain place such as a garden. Describe what he or she must leave behind in the garden. Once it is time to go, describe a certain struggle such as struggling to let a problem go. Perhaps include the courageous task of burying the struggle in the garden. The struggle can be internal such as worry, doubt, fear, or confusion, or it can be external such as a family idol, broken gadget, tarot cards, pornographic photo, or a good luck charm.

2. After entering into the doorway of marriage or dating, years later your character returns to a familiar location and discovers that he or she has courageously overcome a struggle such as impulsive shopping, horoscopes, a critical attitude, being on welfare, gambling, voodoo, gluttony, lust, bitterness, neglect, or hoarding.

3. In a small town, a group of bad people were plotting something terrible. Your character is a spy who builds a friendship with one good person from that small town. You decide how the town will be destroyed, except for the good person and her household. The struggle might be in trusting one good person or fighting off the leader of the bad people in town.

"Be strong and very courageous. Be careful to obey all the instructions Moses gave you. Do not deviate from them, turning either to the right or to the left. Then you will be successful in everything you do" (Joshua 1:7).

4. The grass is always greener on the other side of the fence – or is it? Your character is discontented with his or her life. Seeking out something new and then facing a difficult situation, you decide if your character opens a new door.

5. Your character discovers a doorway to the pasture of happiness. Once reaching the pasture, he or she must courageously face a renovation, either a literal renovation or a figurative renovation, in order to remain. CS Lewis describes it in the following quote:

"Imagine yourself as a living house. God comes in to rebuild that house. At first, perhaps, you can understand what He is doing. He is getting the drains right and stopping the leaks in the roof and so on; you knew that those jobs needed doing and so you are not surprised. But presently He starts knocking the house about in a way that hurts abominably and does not seem to make any sense…You thought you were being made into a decent little cottage: but He is building a palace. He intends to come and live in it Himself." – CS Lewis.

Describe your character's struggle such as almost returning to the place of unhappiness. Perhaps your character will learn contentment, get lost, find rest, or second guess the process of renovation.

6. Alice is too big to fit through the small door. You decide why she is trapped, and you decide how she gets through the small door. Alice in Wonderland is in the public domain, which means you can use the storyline and characters from the story. You decide if you want to select another character name. You decide how you want to be inspired by Lewis Carroll.

7. Set in today's world, your character was despised by his jealous brothers. Perhaps he was sold as a slave to another country. After many years of hard work, your character has risen to power. His brothers arrive to ask for help, not knowing it is their brother they had sold. Since your character has a heart of gold and true love for one another, he forgives his brothers and helps them. You decide what kind of new struggle the brothers face, living with courage to accept grace. This conflict is inspired by the story of Joseph who was sold as a slave to Egypt (Genesis 45-50).

8. Similar to Prospero, your character has stumbled into magic. Someone who he once trusted has betrayed him, leaving him in a tiny boat out in the sea to die. Arriving at an island, he must learn how to not rely on enchantments. He begins to see that good really does win in the end. You decide how he uses his courage to find freedom. Inspired by Prospero from *Temptest.*

9. Other doors that you might want to write about: a secret door that has been hidden for thousands of years, a door that leads to terror, a locked closet door that has something terrible, the doorway to heaven (Jesus), a teleport, or a magical doorway that leads to a different world.

I am the door. If anyone enters by me, he will be saved and will go in and out and find pasture. John 10:9

A word about your setting...

One key to writing a good story is to write what you know, using your natural voice to do it. I believe writers should include a setting that they know about. By this I mean that it is important to reflect on real places you have experienced, value the people you have encountered, and recall the location where you grew up. In order to describe the setting, you must know it. Cherish your childhood culture setting as well as the places where you have traveled. Find ways to let it inspire you when you write.

Even if no one else understands what you are talking about, make a list of childhood settings and adult settings. For example, someone's list might look like the following: green velvet purse, problem on the bus, camping disaster, Aunt Judy's issue, the girl who set the kitchen timer, giving birth with no doctor, hair show, Snoqualmie Falls.

Stories can begin with action or they can begin with a setting. Either way, a writer will need to describe the setting.

1. List several memorable childhood settings.

2. List several memorable adult settings. The key is to list situations that you are passionate about, a meaningful time, an achievement through hard work, a tranquil moment, a life changing moment, a life lesson, a loving moment, or a moment with someone you admire. If it is important to you, you'll be more likely to write about it.

3. What kind of society will be in your setting?

- An unjust society or a just society?
- A supernatural element or a natural world?
- An immoral society or a moral society?
- An "each man to his own" society or a law and order society?
- Unreasonable ambitions? Unreasonable obligations?
- Futuristic
- From history

TRAVELING WITH COURAGE

On the other hand, creative writers have a talented imagination. We can create a totally new place where a new story is set. If you dream at night, you might need to describe the setting as much as you can and fill in where you need to fill in. Either way, you can still tap into what feels somewhat familiar to you in order to create a new world or a different setting. Be sure to describe it as much as possible. Think of it as a photo that you need to describe.

The setting is important, and the reader will need to know where the character is located. One exception to that would be if the writer wants the reader to *not* know where the character is located for the purpose of keeping the reader in suspense until the very end when the reader discovers, for example, that the character had been buried alive.

Where have you traveled? If you are alive, you have a story to tell. Even if you are not much of a traveler, even if you have never moved anywhere, you still have been to places in your town that you can describe.

1. List several places where you have traveled.

2. List a setting that you would like to write about or research.

3. List a new setting that you might like to explore.

WRITE WHAT YOU KNOW

What kind of problems do you see in the world? List three issues that interest you.

What kind of struggle have you or someone else gone through that you want to write about? (death of a loved one, marriage, cults, rioting, going to prison, personal injury or illness, losing a job, feeling lost in retirement, a loss of finances, a difficult pregnancy, parenting, etc.)

How did you/they have the courage to get through it?

Write down ten topics and/or places where you have traveled that you might like to write about or research.

1.
2.
3.
4.
5.
6.
7.
8.
9.
10.

1. DISCOVER A GOOD LESSON

What did you or someone you know discover after going through a crisis? Find a way to make lemonade from lemons. What good came out of it?

How can it help other people?

What did the Holy Spirit teach you? The Holy Spirit is invisible, but He is real. He comforts us, restores our heart, convicts us of sin and righteousness, teaches us what is right and good, and He intercedes for us. He does so much more. He gives the children of God gifts to build up one another.

2. EXPERIENCE

What kind of experience did you have or observe that you want to write about or journal privately?

What did someone else go through that you want other people to learn from?

Each month, we will build onto this list, Write What You Know.

PITCH

If you are a serious fiction writer, you need to know how important it is to write a one sentence summary for your story.

Please take a moment to write a one sentence summary for your story. You can write it at the beginning or at the end of writing your story, but it is preferred if you write it at the beginning of the story. This is excellent practice and something you should get in the habit of doing. Feel free to update it however you need to, let it help you focus on your story, and let it help motivate you to finish your story with a good ending.

This summary is also called a pitch; it is also called a log line.
Writing a one sentence summary is something you should become familiar with so that you can easily tell other people about your story. When you begin to collect a stack of stories a mile high, you will appreciate having a summery at the top of the front page.

A summary should tell three things:
1. WHO is the main character?
2. GOAL - what is the main character's goal?
3. OBSTACLE - what is the character's main obstacle?

Once you practice saying your pitch out loud, you can memorize it quite well and tell other people about it.

If you are going to make a 10-minute appointment with a publisher at a writing conference, then you should have a 5-minute pitch prepared ahead of time. Keep that in mind when you are writing your pitch.

Each month, the chapter will end with a place like this where you can write down your pitch.

The title that you first use for your story is usually called your work-in-progress title. It might become your final title, or you might come up with another title after the story is complete.

Next season, we will add onto this pitch page.

PITCH PAGE

Write a one sentence summary for each one of your stories.
These summaries can be for you to tell your family and friends. They can also be for you to tell agents, publishers, editors, readers, and reviewers.

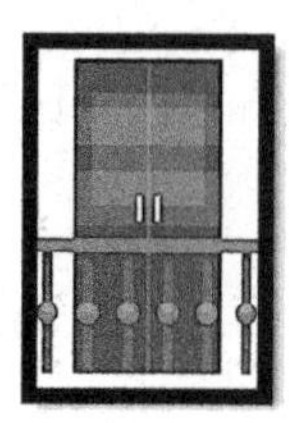

MY PITCH FOR (TITLE, DATE)

1. Who is the main character?

2. What is the main character's goal?

3. What is the character's main obstacle?

MY PITCH

Commit to the Lord whatever you do, and he will establish your plans. – Proverbs 16:3

4. Write a longer pitch version for anyone who is interested in learning more about your story. This can help you with the blurb on the back of the book or a synopsis for a publisher.

Print out your final draft of 750 words. Write your pitch at the top of the page. Fold it in half. Place it here in this workbook. Repeat this process each month.

MONTH TWO TOPIC:

____

OUTSMART THE VILLAIN

Way to go last month! *Welcome to Month Two!* Write the current month and year on the line above. For example, if you began this workbook in January, write "February XXXX (Year)" on the line at the top of this page.

WHAT WILL WE DO IN THIS CHAPTER?

We will be covering the following items: optional conflicts, favorite stories, identify a greedy villain, explore an escape plot, write what you know, and pitches.

DIRECTIONS: (Same each month)

1. On the next page, read the theme, setting, and three highlights.
2. Read through the optional conflicts and circle any that you might want to write about or explore further.
3. Work through the rest of "Month Two" at your own pace. Write your story at any time during the process of steps 1, 2, and 3. Use this workbook as a springboard to write your story. Every month will end the chapter with "Write What You Know" and a place where you can write down your new "Pitch." Try to finish your story by the 25th of the month.

THEME OF GREED

THEME: Greed

SETTING: Your character comes in conflict with a greedy villain. You decide if the villain is pushing sorcery, bribes, extortion, or sexual immorality in order to gain money, fame, or power. You decide who might be the expert in your story, the main character or the villain. You decide who is going to make a promise, a promise that is either kept or broken.

3 HIGHLIGHTS (include): a villain, a promise, and an escape

WORD COUNT: 750-1,500

DEADLINE: 25th of the month

RESOURCES FOR YOU TO EXPLORE:

- *Giant Tales Beyond the Mystic Doors*, Chapter 2: Beasts
- *In the Presence of My Enemies* by Gracia Burnham
- *Consignment Science Fiction Adventures* by Alan Edward Nourse
- *The Feasts of Autolycus: The Diary of a Greedy Woman* by Elizabeth Robins Pennell
- *Granny's Wonderful Chair & Its Tales of Fairy Times* by Frances Browne
- *13 Days: The Chronicle of an Escape from a German Prison* by John Alan Lyde Caunter
- *Trouble and distress have come upon me, but your commands give me delight.* – Psalm 119:143
- Other resources:

OPTIONAL CONFLICTS TO GET YOU STARTED

1. Your character sets out for a particular destination. Along the way, he or she encounters a greedy fortune teller, a villain, who gives bad directions or false information. Your character might find out that he is being set up by the villain. He must figure out a way to outsmart the villain's destructive way, escape the villain, and/or get out of a bad situation.

2. Your character knows a greedy villain who is ruthlessly climbing the corporate ladder. Your character sees the villain robbing, pickpocketing, or stealing. The villain is stealing life from everyone and anyone who is in his or her path. Your character must outsmart the villain, find a way to catch him in the act of being greedy for gain, and/or escape from being the victim.

3. Your character is invited to what seems like an innocent get together or weekend retreat. A nice but very greedy pimp villain attempts to lure your character into giving massages and engaging in prostitution. Your character must outsmart the villain and find a way to escape a bad situation.

4. Your character's neighbor is constantly focused on more, more, more. The conflict becomes personal when a greedy neighbor villain begins to influence your character's spouse! A stranger tells your character that Jesus said, "Watch out! Be on your guard against all kinds of greed. Life does not consist in an abundance of possessions" (Luke 12:15). You decide what happens to the spouse.

5. Your character has been trying to "keep up with the Jones' family." Mr. Jones lives next door, and he has gone all out for Halloween. Your character continually compares himself to Mr. Jones and thinks he has to do better. You decide if Mr. Jones will have a change of heart.

6. Your character has become a wealthy miserable miser. Worrying about losing it all, his possessions constantly tug his mind. His bad habit is that he is always counting the cost. Finally, he goes on a weekend trip to refresh himself. While there, he learns something about living on very little and experiencing what matters most. You describe what kind of retreat he goes on. You describe his experience. You describe what situation teaches him the rewards of giving.

7. Your character is happily married until he or she begins to associate with a card club. Each month, the betting goes higher and higher. A friend warns your character to stop betting so high. Winning several months in a row, your character becomes addicted to gambling. While gambling, a good friend comes to the rescue. After a difficult loss, describe what else causes your character to find a better way to live.

8. Your character is a woman who is unable to calm her political husband. She must find a way to not get involved with her husband's terrible racist way of taking others down on the false pretense of gaining, maintaining, and stabilizing peace. She receives a prophesy that she will need to stand firm and rebuke her husband's greed, racism, and ambition. This conflict is slightly inspired by the story of Esther and Haman (Esther 1-10).

9. Your character and his or her spouse live in a nice neighborhood where a seemingly nice mayor lives. At a card club dessert social, your character finds out that the mayor will be running for the House of Representatives – with a greedy guarantee of winning through a process of fraud. Unlike Macbeth and Lady Macbeth, your character lives by worthy morals. You decide how your character will stop the greedy mayor from winning. Much like Macduff, your character must find a way to help a good mayor replace the bad mayor and stop the bad mayor from winning a seat in the House of Representatives.

10. Your character is a woman who must try to find out if her best friend's husband has repented of his greedy, overbearing, cruel, and jealous way. Your character has been hiding and protecting her best friend for twenty years. Wrongly thinking his wife loves another man, the husband becomes cruel and overbearing to his innocent wife after she gave birth to a baby girl. Your character and her good husband save this innocent woman from her cruel husband. For twenty years, the cruel husband has believed his wife and baby daughter are dead. Your character tells her friend's cruel husband that she made a statue of his wife. Wanting to see it, you describe how the widower reveals his changed heart. Inspired by Shakespeare's characters Hermione and Paulina from *The Winter's Tale.*

11. Other conflicts that you might want to write about: a famous athlete or rock star is greedy for fame, and then loses it all. Starting all over again, he or she finds true happiness.

The greedy stir up conflict, but those who trust in the Lord will prosper. – Proverbs 28:25

FAVORITE STORIES, HEROES, & VILLAINS

Are you a storyteller?

Authors keep on doing what we love to do. We tell our story! Whether there are any book sales or not, authors will feel bottled up unless we tell our story. The need for telling a story will motivate authors who love storytelling.

1. Write down the titles of some of your favorite stories. If the story does not have an official title, make one up.

Every story will need some kind of antagonist. An antagonist is usually a person who actively opposes or is hostile to someone or something. An antagonist can also be called an adversary, opponent, enemy, foe, nemesis, rival, competitor, contradictor, bad person, or villain. The antagonist is one who contends with or opposes another. In literature, the antagonist is usually a character who opposes the story's main character.

2. Write down some of your favorite heroes, protagonists, etc.

3. Write down a few villains that you like to despise.

ANTAGONISTS - From the list below, select a few antagonists that you might want to include in your story.

Terrorist – fearfully a coward, using unlawful violence or intimidation, bomber, arsonist, gunman, assassin, desperado

Rioter – leading an uproar, rampage, disturbance, violet disturbance, commotion, submitting to no one

Denying truth – skeptic, contradictor, cynic, doubter, pessimist, thinking the worst is best

Vile - extremely unpleasant, foul, nasty, disagreeable, horrible, dreadful, abominable

Hateful – murderer, dishonorable, contemptible, scandalous, shameful

Sexually immoral – adultery, prostitution, harlotry, sexual relations between unmarried individuals, lust, pornography, sodomy, rape, homosexuality, incest, fornicator, whoremonger

Sorcery – magic, black magic, witchcraft, wizardry, occultism, casting spells, incantation, necromancy, divination, voodooism, shamanism, demonry, channeling, thaumaturgy

Idolaters – heathen priest, pagan worship, exalting doubt, agnostic, renegade, schismatic, skeptic, apostate, disruptor, iconoclast, heretic

Liars – deceiver, fibber, dishonest gain, perjurer, fabricator, equivocator, mislead on purpose, ambiguous to hide the truth

3 PHASES OF ESCAPING A GREEDY VILLAIN

1. Feeling imprisoned. 2. A plan to escape. 3. The actual escape.

The escape could be an escape from a bad school, unjustly imprisoned, or a horrible job. It could be an escape from a location or an escape from a controlling person. It is a literal physical escape such as an escape from a kidnapper or an escape from a terrorist. It could be an escape from a mob or from a bad marriage. It could be an escape from bad people on an island or an escape from a cult.

Write down an escape plot from a story that you find interesting. Underline anything in the previous paragraph that you might want to explore further.

EXERCISE: Include three phases of an escape plot.

EXAMPLE: ___________Cat and Mouse________________________

1. Being imprisoned – A mouse feels trapped inside the wall.

2. A plan to escape – The mouse plans to escape when the cat is sleeping.

3. The actual escape – The mouse sneaks out in the middle of the night, but an unexpected noise wakes up the cat. The mouse must run for his life.

ESCAPE STORY PRACTICE

EXERCISE: Underline one of the escape settings below that you can work with right now or select another kind of escape setting.

Underline One: A bad school, horrible job, controlling person, kidnapper, terrorist, mob, bad marriage, unjustly imprisoned, bad people on an island, or an escape from a cult. Other:

DIRECTIONS: Include three phases of an escape plot.

1. Being imprisoned

2. A plan to escape

3. The actual escape

CHANGE NAMES

When you write about an experience you or someone else had with a greedy person in real life, remember to change all the names.

You never want defame a person's reputation or end up in a lawsuit over publishing a libel.

WRITE WHAT YOU KNOW

What kind of struggle have you or someone else you know been through?

Where have you traveled recently?

1. DISCOVER A GOOD LESSON

What did you or someone else you know discover during or after a struggle?

What kind of story has inspired you to write about it?

How can it help other people?

2. EXPERIENCE
What kind of experience did you or someone you know go through that you want to write about?

3. ANTAGONIST
What kind of antagonist or villain do you want to write about?

Each month, we will build onto this list.

PITCH

It is important to write a one sentence summary, a pitch, for your story.

Please take a moment to write a one sentence summary for your short story. This is excellent practice and something you should get in the habit of doing each month.

There are several reasons why a pitch is important. You can easily tell other people about your story with a pitch. You will quickly remember what your story is about when referring back to it. Pitches are good for publishers, reviewers, and readers.

A summary should tell three things:
1. WHO is the main character?
2. GOAL - what is the main character's goal?
3. OBSTACLE - what is the character's main obstacle?

Practice saying your pitch out loud and memorize it.

If you are going to make a 10-minute appointment with a publisher at a writing conference, then you ought to have a one sentence pitch ready. You can also prepare a 5-minute pitch prepared ahead of time. What kind of writing conferences are in your area? Start searching for writing conferences that you might want to learn more about.

Next season, we will add onto this pitch page.

PITCH PAGE

Write a one sentence summary for each one of your stories.
These summaries can be for you to tell your family and friends. They can also be for you to tell agents, publishers, editors, readers, and reviewers.

MY PITCH FOR (TITLE, DATE)

1. Who is the main character?

2. What is the main character's goal?

3. What is the character's main obstacle?

MY PITCH

Commit to the Lord whatever you do, and he will establish your plans. – Proverbs 16:3

4. Write a longer pitch version for anyone who is interested in learning more about your story.

Print out your final draft. Write your pitch at the top of the page. Fold it in half. Place it here in this workbook. Repeat this process each month.

MONTH THREE TOPIC:

APPOINTMENTS

Good job on the first two months! Now you're starting to get the hang of it. I hope you are printing out your stories. You should have at least two stories in this workbook. Fasten your stories in this workbook by using a paper clip. When you carry this workbook with you, you can read your pitches to anyone and ask people to read your 3-minute story. Carefully ask them what they think about it.

Welcome to *Month Three!*

WHAT WILL WE DO IN THIS CHAPTER?

We will be covering the following items: optional conflicts, appointments, grabbing the reader's attention (a hook), write what you know, and pitches.

DIRECTIONS: (Same each month)

1. On the next page, read the theme, setting, and three highlights.
2. Read through the optional conflicts and circle any that interest you.
3. Work through the rest of the workbook in "Month Three." Use the workbook as a springboard to write your story. Every month will end with "Write What You Know" and a place where you can write down your new pitch. Try to finish your story by the 25th of each month.

THEME OF ACCEPTANCE

THEME: Acceptance

SETTING: Your character has an appointment that triggers a certain outcome. You decide on the location - if the appointment is at an office, vacation spot, or house. Most of your story can take place before the appointment, at the appointment, or after the appointment. You decide.

3 HIGHLIGHTS (include): An appointment (get together, meeting, or a scheduled vacation), a piece of writing in print, and a flower

WORD COUNT: 750-1,500

DEADLINE: 25th of the month

RESOURCES FOR YOU TO EXPLORE:

- *Giant Tales Beyond the Mystic Doors*, Chapter 3: Sunflowers
- *Joni: An Unforgettable Story* by Joni Eareckson Tada
- *At the Appointed Time* by A. Maynard Barbour
- *Appointment in Tomorrow* by Fritz Leiber
- *Gradual Acceptance of the Copernican Theory of the Universe* by Dorothy Stimson
- *Great Acceptance: The Life Story of F. N. Charrington* by Guy Thorne
- *Do not be anxious about anything, but in every situation, by prayer and petition, with thanksgiving, present your requests to God.* – Philippians 4:6
- Other resources:

OPTIONAL CONFLICTS TO GET YOU STARTED

1. Your character has an appointment with a psychologist because he or she is not doing well. Feeling melancholy during the appointment, the psychologist gives a diagnosis of isolation, having a sense of loneliness. Describe how the psychologist empowers your character to gain a sense of purpose, break free from any perceived racial ideologies or injustices, and/or leave behind the feeling of not belonging.

2. No gift. No phone call. Feeling hurt and distant from his or her own children, your impatient character keeps hoping they'll come around. Even though your character is busy at work, he plans a fun family vacation that his kids will like. Describe a scene from the family vacation and how it helped your character find the benefit of quality time, serving, and/or giving.

3. Your character does not think he or she needs to prune the front yard. Overgrown bushes make it difficult to get to the front door. A nice neighbor manages to ring the doorbell one day, but your character forgot how to be kind. Describe a change of heart when he is given another opportunity to help and/or interact with his neighbor.

4. Your character moves to a new town or has been in the same town for way too long. Every time he or she tries to fit in, something goes wrong. At a lunch appointment, your character finds out something terrible that has been going on in town. Describe how your character will overcome feelings of insecurity, find harmony, and/or bust open a crime.

5. Your character is a young woman from Central America whose parents decide to sell her for $10,000 to a coyote in order to have a better life in the USA. Are her high hopes unrealistic? Will she ever achieve a better life? You decide what happens after she leaves home with the coyote.

6. Your character is a woman who fell in love with a man and he proposed to her, but she has already been married and divorced two times. The woman is not convinced that she should ever get married again, but a relative tells her that marriage will help her feel complete.

7. Your character is a journalist who must confront a rioter who justifies destroying federal statues. Using hate to stir up riots, the rioter plans to destroy more federal statues. You decide how the rioter ends up in jail for a crime he did not commit. You decide what the journalist says to the rioter in jail. You decide if the rioter begins to forgive rioters and whether he has to serve any jail time. Inspired by the story of the unmerciful, unforgiving servant (Matthew 18:21-35).

8. Your character is constantly in conflict with a difficult person at school. When visiting the school counselor, your character discusses his or her feelings about being bullied and mistreated by another classmate. Since it has become an issue in the entire school, your character convinces the school to roll out a "Brown Eye, Blue Eye Game" over three days. On day one, all the brown-eyed students are favored. On day two, all the blue-eyed students are favored. On day three, describe all the wonderful lessons that all the students learned except for the bully. You decide if the governor issues a mandatory Brown Eye, Blue Eye day in all schools across the state. You decide if the bully finally comes around to accepting one another.

9. Wanting to feel accepted, your character begins to run with the wrong kind of crowd such as a gang or a cult. You decide how he or she finally realizes it is time to say goodbye to bad influences. You decide what kind of divine meeting changed his or her life.

10. Your character wants to discover what he or she should do with his or her life. Learning about a career counselor who might be able to help, describe what happens at the appointment. You decide if he takes a helpful aptitude test or a useless aptitude test. You describe if he or she makes use of his or her skills and talents. You decide if your character begins to understand what it means to have the attitude and heart of a servant.

11. Other conflicts you might want to write about: dealing with rejection, feeling a sense of belonging, accepting that reality is good, accepting that God is good, accepting the laws of logic, accepting that the universe had a beginning.

Accept one another, then, just as Christ accepted you, in order to bring praise to God. – Romans 15:7

STRESSFUL APPOINTMENTS

Have you ever experienced a stressful appointment? A time when you went to a funeral, met a business associate, or felt nervous about a job situation? Write down any words, names, or instances that you might want to write about.

1. Death of a loved one

2. Business associate

3. Marriage

4. Work related troubles: getting fired, heavy workload, lack of organization, etc.

SERIOUS MATTERS

Consider an appointment where your character must discuss a serious matter. Write down at least one situation that comes to mind, related to these serious matters, that you or someone you know has been through. Circle any of the following matters that you might want to write or journal about:

- moving to a new town
- an injury
- illness
- financial troubles
- age transition from childhood to adulthood
- over the hill
- retirement

1. Death of a loved one (Princess Diana died in 1997.)

2. Political scandal (President Richard Nixon was charged with obstruction of Justice and abuse of power in 1974.)

3. Marriage (Elvis married Priscilla in 1967.)

4. Work related troubles: getting fired, heavy workload, lack of organization

5. Other serious matters ___________________

In order to gain the reader's attention, you will need to include the following items: 1.) Introduce the character's goal or passion, 2.) Present an obstacle or problem, and 3.) Leave the reader wanting to find out what is going to happen.

As the writer, you will need to present a troubling incident that sets the story into motion. On the next page, we will explore how to grab the reader's attention in more detail.

GRABBING THE READER'S ATTENTION

Early in the story, you will need to grab the reader's attention. This can be done if you introduce the character, the problem, and find a way to *hook* the reader into wanting to find out what is going to happen. When you grab the reader's attention, it is called a *hook*. It could be just one sentence or a few sentences. It should ideally be on the front page of the story or right at the beginning.

EXAMPLE 1: Let's say your character is a woman who fell in love with a man and he proposed to her, but she has already been married and divorced two times. The woman is not convinced that she should ever get married again, but a relative tells her that marriage will help her feel complete. A neighbor friend, having a bad attitude about men in general, tells the woman she should never get married again because all men are either pimps or control freaks. The woman does not want to lose her boyfriend, but she enjoys being single. She worries that he will end up divorcing her like her other two x-husbands did. Your story is about a woman who makes an appointment with a psychologist to talk about whether she should get married again. That is enough information for the reader to *want to find out if she is going to get married or not.* It also leaves the reader wanting to find out if the woman will ever get over her fear of getting married and other misconceptions about marriage. The reader might even begin to wonder why her two x-husbands divorced her.

1. The character: A woman who has been divorced two times.

2. The main problem: Her boyfriend proposed to her, but she is confused about whether she should get married.

3. Other problems: A relative and a neighbor are giving the woman bad advice. The woman is afraid of getting divorced again. The woman might love her single life more than being married.

4. The main hook: Will the woman get married for the third time or not? Other hooks: If she marries again, will it work out?

EXAMPLE 2: Let's say your character is a young woman from Central America whose parents decide to sell her for $10,000 to a coyote in order to have a better life in the USA. Are her high hopes unrealistic? Will she ever achieve a better life? The day is scheduled for her to say good-bye to her homeland. She keeps her appointment with the coyote. The young woman travels with a human trafficker, even though smuggling is a crime, and she feels like she's been kidnapped. Your story is about the young woman who trusts a coyote, but she endures beatings, starvation, heat exhaustion, and small overcrowded sleeping areas. She might be forced to participate with the drug cartel and human trafficking. The coyote threatens to mistreat her family back home unless she cooperates. The young woman faces many dangerous situations on the journey. Where will she end up? Will her life ever get better? Will the terrible memories ever go away? Hopefully, the reader will want to find out if the woman will survive the terrible journey and whether or not her life will be any better if she ever arrives at a new home.

1. The character: A young woman who travels with a coyote to experience a better life.
2. The main problem: Feeling kidnapped, she encounters many dangerous situations that delay the journey.
3. Other problems: The young woman must find a way to escape drug cartels and human trafficking.
4. The main hook: Will the young woman ever reach her final destination of having a better life?
5. Another hook: Once she arrives at her new home, will it be any better than the life she left behind?

PRACITCE: STORY CONFLICT AND HOOK

DIRECTIONS: Select one of the optional conflicts from this month.

1. Who is your main character?

2. What is his or her problem?

3. What are several different outcomes that might happen?

How will you *hook* the reader into wanting to find out what will happen?

WRITE WHAT YOU KNOW

What kind of struggle have you or someone else you know been through?

Have you traveled anywhere recently? Reflect on a place where you traveled.

1. DISCOVER A GOOD LESSON

What did you or someone else you know discover during or after a struggle?

What did you learn?

How can it help other people?

2. EXPERIENCE

What kind of experience did you or someone you know go through that you want to write about?

3. ANTAGONIST

What kind of antagonist do you want to write about?

4. APPOINTMENTS

Have you ever experienced a unique conversation that is memorable? Write down any words or instances that you might want to write about.

Each month, we will build onto this list.

PITCH

If you are a serious fiction writer, you know how important it is to write a one sentence summary for your story.

Please take a moment to write a one sentence summary for your short story. This is excellent practice and something you should get in the habit of doing.

This summary is also called a pitch; it is also called a log line.
This one sentence summary is something you should become familiar with and even memorize so that you can easily tell other people about your story.

A summary should tell three things:
1. WHO is the main character?
2. GOAL - what is the main character's goal?
3. OBSTACLE - what is the character's main obstacle?

Once you practice saying your pitch out loud, you can memorize it quite easily.

If you are going to make a 10-minute appointment with a publisher at a writing conference, then you ought to have a 5-minute pitch prepared ahead of time. Think about opening your appointment with something short and catchy. You could begin with describing your story as a mix between two well-known stories, but then you'll need to explain what you mean by that.

Next season, we will add onto this pitch page.

PITCH PAGE

Write a one sentence summary for each one of your stories.
These summaries can be for you to tell your family and friends. They can also be for you to tell agents, publishers, editors, readers, and reviewers.

MY PITCH FOR (TITLE, DATE)

---

1. Who is the main character?

2. What is the main character's goal?

3. What is the character's main obstacle?

MY PITCH

Commit to the Lord whatever you do, and he will establish your plans. – Proverbs 16:3

4. Write a longer pitch version for anyone who is interested in learning more about your story.

Print out your final draft. Write your pitch at the top of the page. Fold it in half. Place it here in this workbook. Repeat this process each month.

SEASON TWO TOPICS FOR MONTHS 4, 5, & 6

Month Four: DISTURBING CONFLICTS

Month Five: MISTY SWAMP

Month Six: UNUSUAL WEATHER

Welcome to season two! Last season, we explored writing what you know, developing good settings, outsmarting a villain, working with an escape plot, identifying stressful appointments, grabbing the reader's attention, and being able to tell our pitch to other people. Good job! We are off to a great start.

This season, we will build on to the development of good storytelling. Without forgetting any of the important aspects from season one, we will continue to write another story and boost our writer's toolbox. For the next three months, we will examine conflict, corruption, and atmosphere.

OUTLINE FOR SEASON TWO: MONTHS 4, 5, & 6 TOPICS

Month Four Topic: Disturbing Conflicts

A. Conflict Structure
B. Types of Conflicts
C. Motives and Reasons
D. *What if…?*

Month Five Topic: Misty Swamp

A. Types of corruption
B. Details in a Swamp
C. Tools for Conflict and Detail

Month Six Topic: Unusual Weather

A. Tools for Atmosphere

MONTH FOUR TOPIC:

____

DISTURBING CONFLICTS

You finished season one! Hooray! I hope you have printed out at least three stories and fastened them into this workbook with a paper clip. Carry this workbook around with you. Do not lose it. Tell people your three pitches. Ask them which one they like best. Ask them to read one of your 3-minute stories. Ask them what they like about it. Thank them for their time.

At the top of this page, write the name of the month and year on the line.

Welcome to *Month Four!*

WHAT WILL WE DO IN THIS CHAPTER?

We will be covering the following items: optional conflicts, disturbing conflicts, types of conflicts, motives, what if…?, write what you know, and pitches.

DIRECTIONS: (Same each month)

1. On the next page, read the theme, setting, and three highlights.
2. Read through the optional conflicts and circle any you are interested in.
3. Work through the rest of "Month Four." Use the workbook as a springboard to write your story. Every month will end with "Write What You Know" and a place where you can write down your new pitch. Try to finish your story by the 25th of each month.

THEME OF OPTIMISM

THEME: Optimism

SETTING: Start your story with a disturbance. Your character is passionate about a certain goal, but a conflict is making it difficult. The goal might be in the performing arts, in athletics, music, politics, law enforcement, gardening, cooking, or in something else of your choosing. The opposition might be a criminal, disgruntled employee, death of a loved one, or an immoral acquaintance. An important message helps your character find optimism and persevere in spite of the obstacle.

3 HIGHLIGHTS (include): A box or gift, an optimistic message, and a conflict

WORD COUNT: 750-1,500

DEADLINE: 25th of the month

RESOURCES FOR YOU TO EXPLORE:

- *Giant Tales Beyond the Mystic Doors*, Chapter 4: Mysterious Boxes
- *Poems of Optimism* by Ella Wheeler Wilcox
- *Mary Lee the Red Cross Girl* by Helen Hart
- *New Optimism* by Henry De Vere Stacpoole, author of *The Blue Lagoon*
- *But you, Lord, are a shield around me, my glory, the One who lifts my head high.* – Psalm 3:3
- Other resources:

OPTIONAL CONFLICTS TO GET YOU STARTED

1. Your character is a single person who goes to work and discovers that his or her boss has suddenly died the night before. Police arrive at the small business to question everyone who worked with your boss. Since your character is single, he or she has no alibi. Your character looks guilty but must remain optimistic. You decide possible motives for the co-workers. You decide who killed the boss and why.

2. Your character loses his or her beloved job. While down in the dumps, he receives a message to help him look on the bright side. He starts a new job doing something unusual such as packing boxes in a completely different field. You describe internal conflicts, decide how the new job turns out, and whether he returns to his old career.

3. Your character carries a terrible secret such as accidentally killing someone in a car crash. Years later, a new neighbor bully happens to be a relative of the deceased person. This neighbor bully keeps making life difficult until an important message stops the neighbor from bullying. Your character almost seeks revenge on the neighbor bully until a box arrives with something inside to help your character remain optimistic.

4. Your character has been living with the true belief that a certain family member is troubled or messed up. As a wake-up call, a good friend somehow reveals to your character that he or she needs to make an effort to do acts of kindness toward that troubled, messed up relative. Show how your character begins to admit his critical, apathetic part either to himself, in a journal, or to a trustworthy friend. You describe how the acts of kindness really begin to help the troubled, messed up person.

5. Your character is a secular psychologist who teaches his or her clients how to overcome stress and conflict. He teaches them to be a peacemaker. All is well until one day, he faces a terrible conflict of his own. He finds out that his peacemaking skills are limited. He learns to value other ways to overcome conflict such as forgiveness and even prayer and faith.

6. Someone famous is facing a major crisis after losing a loved one. Motivated at the funeral, he or she coordinates a conference on whether or not there is such a thing as an afterlife. Your character has been asked to speak as a philosopher at this conference. The topic is on whether or not God had a beginning. After explaining that Bertrand Russell was illogical to think that God must have had a beginning, you decide if your character can explain what it means to live in time and how it differs from living outside of time. You decide how the famous person reacts to the history of Jesus who experienced an afterlife for three days and then rose from the dead.

7. Your character is helping a friend who is having a mid-life crisis. This friend does not think that his self exists. He is unable to discern if he is in a dream world. Your character tries to present Rene Descartes' optimistic statement, "I think, therefore I am." Your friend is uncertain about it, wondering if he could be thinking but not existing. As a realist, your character must find other ways to convince your friend that he exists.

8. Your character is helping a friend who is having a mid-life crisis. This friend sold everything and now lives as a traveling gypsy who is a fortune teller. Knowing that these fortune teller appointments are a fake, your character visits his or her friend in order to try and offer some help. You decide if your character can get through. You decide if biblical prophecy might help get the friend back on track.

9. Your character is having a mid-life crisis, wondering if the universe had a beginning. He begins to doubt everything unless he can see it. Thinking God is no different than an invisible made-up dragon, he begins to live as if materialism is all that exists - and that God does not exist. When a good friend suddenly passes away, your character is faced with the life after death concept at his friend's funeral. You decide how your character responds to the origin of the universe, the origin of life, the resurrection of Jesus Christ, and his friend's life after death.

10. Other conflicts you might want to write about: work related stress, physical appearance, social pressures, competition, health worries, moving to a new city, a spouse's death, financial worries, lack of personal breathing space, or a traumatic past event.

And we know that in all things God works for the good of those who love him, who have been called according to his purpose. – Romans 8:28

CONFLICT STRUCTURE

In order for a story to be interesting, it must have a conflict. Some conflicts are more disturbing than other conflicts. The highest level of conflict includes the possible risk of death. Your job as a writer is to connect - in a passionate way - with a certain conflict. With numerous conflicts to choose from, you'll be sure to find one to write about. A good writer should practice working with the structure of a conflict. Whether you like story outlines or not, you will at least need a good conflict. A typical conflict structure usually has three main parts.

1. A problem is presented.

2. An attempt is made to solve the problem.

3. The problem gets resolved.

EXERCISE: Select any conflict you are familiar with, concerned about, or you might be interested in. You can select one of the optional conflicts from the previous list. One key to writing a good story is to recognize the fact that you are passionate about a certain topic. Now use the structure format listed above to develop a conflict structure. This is just for practice. This exercise should help you get to know the details of your story.

1. Problem:

2. Attempt to solve the problem:

3. Resolution:

TYPES OF CONFLICTS

EXERCISE: Select one of the following conflicts that you might want to work with or add one of your own from the previous page. Write down three parts to the conflict.

- A hero must conquer a physical monster.
- Being forced to deal with or confront someone's trouble.
- Yearning for a goal, but obstacles are in the way.
- Other:

1. What is the main character's problem? Additional problems?

2. What attempt is made to solve the problem?

3. What are at least two different possible outcomes?

MOTIVES AND REASONS

The protagonist and antagonist both have a reason for doing what they are doing. Select one of the following motives to work with or develop one of your own. This time, explain either the protagonist's problem or the antagonist's problem.

- A villain is angry over a traumatic childhood experience.
- The protagonist has a professional duty or a moral duty to intervene – he must stop a criminal.
- The protagonist is the only one equipped to get the job done.
- A villain enjoys doing something bad because he was brought up that way.
- A villain is hurt over the loss of a loved one.
- The protagonist was adopted and uses it as an excuse to feel like he or she does not belong.
- The protagonist is critical and blames it on his environment.

EXERCISE: Use one of the motives above to write out a conflict structure for either the protagonist or the antagonist.

1. What is the character's main problem?

2. What attempt is made to solve the problem?

3. What are at least two different options for the outcome?

WHAT IF...?

EXERCISE: Reflect on a real experience you had that stands out for some reason. Write it down and include everything you can about it. Just as if you were writing in a journal or talking to someone, write down everything that happened from beginning to end. Do not leave anything out.

This really happened:

EXERCISE: Once you finally finish one paragraph or a two-page story, go back and start asking, "What if…?" You can add drama by slightly changing a few things. For maximum conflict, you might ask, "What if I almost died?" Remember to change the names of real people in order to avoid any real conflict down the road.

What if…?

HE STOLE MY DRINK

EXAMPLE: Let me reflect on a real experience I had at lunch.
I placed a lunch order using an app. When I arrived at the restaurant, I noticed a man in front of me reaching for a drink on the to-go table. It looked as though he might be taking my drink, but I was not sure. He walked away with the drink. Concerned, I walked up to the table and read the receipt on the bag. It had my name on it. At that moment, I was certain that the man took my drink. Not sure if he made an innocent mistake or if he took it on purpose, I said nothing. I wasn't sure what to do. For a moment, I was speechless. Do I run after the man who took my drink? By that time, the man had opened the door and left. Walking over to the counter, I explained what just happened. Next, brainstorm by asking, What if…?

- What if…a villain is seeking revenge against a restaurant owner?
- What if… a terrorist organization in town is looking for a restaurant they can bully?
- What if… I ran after the man and confronted him, but he pulled a gun out and told me to get lost? Over a drink? Why did he do that?

EXERCISE: Add a "What if…" of your own:

What if…

WRITE WHAT YOU KNOW

What kind of struggle have you or someone else you know been through?

Where have you traveled recently?

1. DISCOVER A GOOD LESSON

What did you or someone else you know discover during or after a struggle?

What did you learn?

How can it help other people?

2. EXPERIENCE

What kind of experience did you or someone you know go through that you want to write about?

3. ANTAGONIST

What kind of antagonist do you want to write about?

4. APPOINTMENT

List a memorable appointment, situation, meeting, or conversation you had recently. Maybe someone else had a meeting or you overheard someone else's conversation.

Each month, we will build onto this list.

PITCHES & WRITING CONFERENCES

Please take a moment to write a one sentence summary for your short story. This is excellent practice and something you should get in the habit of doing.

A summary should tell three things:
1. WHO is the main character?
2. GOAL - what is the main character's goal?
3. OBSTACLE - what is the character's main obstacle?

If you are going to make a 10-minute appointment with a publisher at a writing conference, then you ought to have a 5-minute pitch prepared ahead of time. Think about opening your appointment with something short and catchy. You could begin with describing your story as a mix between two well-known stories, but then you'll need to explain what you mean by that.

List any writing conferences coming up that you might want to attend:

1.

2.

3.

PITCH PAGE

Write a one sentence summary for each one of your stories.
These summaries can be for you to tell your family and friends. They can also be for you to tell agents, publishers, editors, readers, and reviewers.

MY PITCH FOR (TITLE, DATE)

1. Who is the main character?

2. What is the main character's goal?

3. What is the character's main obstacle?

MY PITCH

Commit to the Lord whatever you do, and he will establish your plans. – Proverbs 16:3

4. Write a longer pitch version for anyone who is interested in learning more about your story.

Print out your final draft. Write your pitch at the top of the page. Fold it in half. Place it here in this workbook. Repeat this process each month.

MONTH FIVE TOPIC:

MISTY SWAMP

You have finished four stories so far! Hooray! Did you ask anyone to read your 3-minute story? What did they say? Which story do they like best so far? Did you write down what they told you? If the feedback was helpful, make sure to write it down. If the feedback was not helpful, then by all means, forget about their comment. Focus on helpful feedback. Find good encouragement. I hope you make an effort to print out your story and paper clip them into this workbook as a way to stay motivated to write another story.

Welcome to *Month Five!*

WHAT WILL WE DO IN THIS CHAPTER?

We will be covering the following items: optional conflicts, types of corruption, corrupt villains, corrupt mafia, characteristics of a swamp, your story's conflict, Cajun restaurant example, write what you know, and pitches.

DIRECTIONS: (Same each month)

1. On the next page, read the theme, setting, and three highlights.
2. Read through the optional conflicts and circle any you are interested in.
3. Read through the next item, "Corrupt Villains." Work through the rest of the chapter. Every month will end with "Write What You Know" and a place where you can write down your new pitch. Try to finish your story by the 25th of each month.

THEME OF CORRUPTION

THEME: Corruption

SETTING: A swamp, wetland, bayou, or preserve

3 HIGHLIGHTS (include): An amphibian or reptile, a maple tree, and an old friend

WORD COUNT: 750-1,500

DEADLINE: 25th of the month

RESOURCES:

- *Giant Tales From the Misty Swamp,* Chapter 1: Misty Swamp
- *Crime and Corruption* by Samuel Vaknin
- *The Man That Corrupted Hadleyburg* by Mark Twain
- *Atrocious Judges: Lives of Judges Infamous as Tools of Tyrants and Instruments of Oppression* by Baron John Campbell
- *Asgard Stories: Tales from Norse Mythology* by Mable H. Cummings and Mary H. Foster
- *I waited patiently for the Lord, He turned to me and heard my cry. He lifted me out of the slimy pit, out of the mud and mire; He set my feet on a rock and gave me a firm place to stand. He put a new song in my mouth, a hymn of praise to our God. Many will see and fear the Lord and put their trust in Him.* – Psalm 40:103
- Other resources:

OPTIONAL CONFLICTS TO GET YOU STARTED

1. Two police partners started off investigating mafia criminals in New Orleans, but somewhere along the process, they gave in to serving as hitmen for the mafia, participating in crimes such as extortion, racketeering, and obstruction of justice. The two policemen are villains, manipulating the system in order to gain financially. Your protagonist finds a way to collect evidence and convict them.

2. Your main character works at a Cajun restaurant. He or she must figure out who is stealing food and drinks and why they are being stolen. He must observe the to-go table and see who might be taking food without paying for it. Several people arrive, but they all have paid for their orders. Soon enough, a man walks in and heads straight for the to-go orders that are sitting on the table. He picks up a bag of food as if it belonged to him and then heads for the door. You decide what happens.

3. Your character takes a vacation to Louisiana. All is going well until he or she happens to run into an old friend. You decide why the old friend has it out to ruin your character's day. You decide how your character gets the old friend off his or her back: walk away, run away, or turn him in to the police.

4. Your character is a wise history professor, chosen to meet with forensics to discuss a swastika that has been seared into a dead man's arm. Your character happens to know the identity of the dead man, an old friend. Convinced that his old friend is innocent, the professor finds out that the police thinks the old friend was guilty of genocide and killed by a group of vigilantes. Your character tracks down one of the vigilantes and decides if the vigilantes have been committing genocide, and if the old friend is innocent.

5. Your character takes a canoe into the wetlands when he or she discovers a hut. Sneaking up on the hut, your character discovers an interesting, dreadful, or frightening situation such as human trafficking or a plan to take over the world. You decide how many people are involved. You decide what happens.

6. Your character encounters a corrupt person. The villain has a lot in common with a corrupt Shakespeare character such as Polonius, Claudius, or Hamlet who thrive on power. Set your story in today's world. Describe any injustice or lack of rule of law that causes a moral or financial hardship. You decide how justice is served.

7. Your good-looking character, becoming a successful man or woman, has been diligently working for a political leader, government machine, or government official. Your story will parallel the story of Joseph and Potiphar's corrupt wife (Genesis 39-41), but set your story in today's world where the rule of law exists. Not getting what she wants, Potiphar's wife lies as a form of revenge, motivated by selfishness and greed. You decide if your character is sent to prison for a crime he did not commit. If so, you decide how he gets out.

8. Your character can no longer turn a blind eye to corruption being inflicted on poor innocent people. Your character is given the task of doing a fraud audit on a corrupt person. You decide if the villain is involved with insider trading, illegal bidders, forced merchandise, machine hacking, or any other kind of fraud. You decide if your character can collect enough evidence to convict the criminal. You decide how the case turns out.

9. With corrupt judges at the highest level, your character lives in a society where justice cannot be served. Describe how the absence of institutional mechanisms affect your character and the people in that society. Your character must become the political competition that improves civilization.

10. Your character carries around a terribly heavy baggage of guilt. No matter how hard he or she tries to do good things, the baggage of guilt creeps up again and again. Seeking different ways to find peace, nothing seems to get rid of the anxiety long term. After experiencing uncertainty to a paralyzing degree, your character visits an old friend in a swamp who lives a holy life. This old friend tells him about a Savior who paid the penalty for all his wrongdoings. Your character begins to believe that this Savior named Jesus can give him peace. On the way home, your character realizes his baggage of guilt is gone. Describe how free he feels. You decide how he begins to share the news with others – that this Savior paid the penalty for all his wrongdoings – and that he has been set free.

10. Other conflicts you might want to write about: embezzlement, bribery, fraud, extortion, or favoritism.

Do not be misled: "Bad company corrupts good character." – 1 Corinthians 15:33

TYPES OF CORRUPTION

When you introduce your antagonist, it is important to identify less-than-admirable behaviors. Why? The reader will want to know. Politicians, policemen, and judges might ignore corruption if given a bribe. The definition of corruption is the action of destroying fidelity or integrity, the abuse of public office for private gain, or making someone or something morally depraved. A dishonest conduct of someone typically in power can lead to devastating consequences.

Corruption can occur in the following locations: a business transaction, corruption in government, law enforcement, or education, corruption in health care, or simple bribery.

CAUSES OF CORRUPTION:

Underline any of the following items that interest you. Add additional causes that you might want to explore. Return to this page on another day and see if your character might struggle with any one of the following:

- Greed for a wealthy kind of living
- Revenge
- Selfishness
- Low political competition
- Weak civil society
- Absence of institutional mechanisms that deal with corruption
- No rule of law
- Wanting to get paid by bribes
- Few are willing to swim against the tide to catch the corrupt person
- Other causes:

CORRUPT VILLAINS – Select all the villains that you might possibly like to write about. Add any others that might come to mind. Which one specifically do you want to write about? You might want to take another day to select just one. Select one of the following types of corrupt villains to include in your story or come up with one of your own:

- o A villain in power destroys a town by shutting down electricity.
- o A villain is manipulating the system to increase his fortune.
- o A villain is climbing the ladder by falsification and/or cheating.
- o Someone evil is flirting to set up an innocent person.
- o A thief is stealing in order to gain material possessions for himself.
- o An adulterer ruins another person's relationship.
- o A mean boss is causing oppression to the workers.
- o A betrayer breaks his or her promise, becoming a disloyal villain.
- o A charming but dishonest villain is power hungry for more.
- o The villain is a control freak about controlling food.
- o A gossip enjoys snooping and spreading rumors to gain attention.
- o A villain with a mental illness copes with it in terrible ways.
- o A narcissist's self-absorption tramples on everyone around.
- o A villain uses other people to gain influence, money, or vacations.
- o Other:

CORRUPTION: MAFIA OR RIOTERS

EXERCISE: Read the following story summary. Select either the mafia or rioting criminals as your villains. Describe how your protagonist gets involved. Explore at least two different outcomes.

> Two police partners started off investigating the mafia or rioting criminals. The partners happened to give in to criminal activity, participating in crime, possibly becoming hitmen or leaders of rioting. The two policemen become villains working for the mafia or riot leaders, manipulating the system in order to gain financially. Your protagonist finds a way to collect evidence to convict them.

1. Did the partners investigate the mafia or rioting criminals or some other kind of criminal activity?

2. How does your protagonist get involved? How does he or she identify or track the partners? What is the incident that moves your protagonist forward?

3. What are at least two different outcomes of the conflict?

CHARACTERISTICS OF A SWAMP

After selecting a conflict, the setting can be enhanced if you make a list of words, phrases, or terms that relate to the kind of atmosphere you are trying to develop.

EXAMPLE: If I want my story to be set in a swamp, I could make a list of words and terms that relate to swamps. Then I can use them in my story.

- Forested wetland, conservation area, protected area
- Ecosystem with fertile soil and numerous birds
- Dominated by tall evergreen trees, mangrove trees, moss hanging from branches, or duckweeds
- Surrounded by water, unaffected by floods, absorbs excess water,
- Connected to a river or lake
- Rich with frogs, alligators, amphibians, or other reptiles
- Found in the southeastern region of the US, also found between the Tigris and Euphrates rivers in Asia, and on every continent except Antarctica.
- Other ideas related to a swamp that you might include or want to research further:

ADD DETAIL TO A STORY

EXERCISE: Select an optional conflict to work with right now. Then answer the following questions.

1. What is the conflict in the story?

2. How does he or she attempt to solve the problem?

3. What are at least two different outcomes of the conflict (to hook the reader)?

4. Make a list of terms, topics, or sources of inspiration that will help you add detail to this story.

CAJUN RESTAURANT – What if…?

EXERCISE: Read the following story. Underline any part of the story that you do not like. Circle any part where you would like to change it. Perhaps you want to change the ending. Place a star where you might want to add something. Write down what you want to add. Ask yourself, "What if…?" at any point along the way in the story. Then answer the following questions.

In this story, the main character is an investigator who gets a call from a Cajun restaurant. The investigator must figure out who is stealing food and drinks and why they are being stolen. He sits at the restaurant, waiting for lunch the next day. Several people arrive, but they all have paid for their orders. Soon enough, a man walks in and heads straight for the to-go orders sitting on the table. He picks up a bag of food as if it belonged to him and then heads for the door. The investigator follows him outside and questions the man. The man lies and says he paid for the food. The investigator tells him that if he does not have a receipt next time, he will be arrested for stealing the food. The investigator also informs the man where he can get free food and drinks for people who have an insufficient source of income.

1. What is the main character's problem/conflict?

2. How does he or she attempt to solve the problem?

3. What are at least two different outcomes for this story?

4. List any other *What if…?* that comes to mind.

WRITE WHAT YOU KNOW

What kind of struggle have you or someone else you know been through?

Where have you traveled recently?

1. DISCOVER A GOOD LESSON

What did you or someone else you know discover during or after a struggle?

What did you learn?

How can it help other people?

2. EXPERIENCE

What kind of experience did you or someone you know go through that you want to write about?

3. ANTAGONIST

What kind of antagonist do you want to write about?

4. APPOINTMENT

List an appointment, meeting, situation, or conversation you or someone else had, learned about, or overheard recently.

5. HOOK

List several outcomes for your story in order to hook your reader into wanting to find out what is going to happen.

6. WHAT IF?

Write down a real situation you experienced, but then add drama by asking, *What if…?*

Each month, we will build onto this list.

PITCHES & WRITING CONFERENCES

Please take a moment to write a one sentence summary for your short story. This is excellent practice and something you should get in the habit of doing.

A summary should tell three things:
1. WHO is the main character?
2. GOAL - what is the main character's goal?
3. OBSTACLE - what is the character's main obstacle?

Once you practice saying your pitch out loud, you can memorize it quite easily.

If you are going to make a 10-minute appointment with a publisher at a writing conference, then you ought to have a 5-minute pitch prepared ahead of time. Think about opening your appointment with something short and catchy. You could begin with describing your story as a mix between two well-known stories, but then you'll need to explain what you mean by that.

List any writing conferences coming up that you might want to attend:

1.

2.

3.

PITCH PAGE

Write a one sentence summary for each one of your stories.
These summaries can be for you to tell your family and friends. They can also be for you to tell agents, publishers, editors, readers, and reviewers.

MY PITCH FOR (TITLE, DATE)

1. Who is the main character?

2. What is the main character's goal?

3. What is the character's main obstacle?

MY PITCH

Commit to the Lord whatever you do, and he will establish your plans. – Proverbs 16:3

4. Write a longer pitch version for anyone who is interested in learning more about your story.

Print out your final draft. Write your pitch at the top of the page. Fold it in half. Place it here in this workbook. Repeat this process each month.

MONTH SIX TOPIC:

UNUSUAL WEATHER

You're almost half-way done. I hope you have at least five short stories fastened into this workbook. Hooray! Good job. Stick with it.

Welcome to *Month Six!*

WHAT WILL WE DO IN THIS CHAPTER?

We will be covering the following items: optional conflicts, tools for creating better atmosphere, write what you know, and pitches.

DIRECTIONS: (Same each month)

1. On the next page, read the theme, setting, and three highlights.
2. Read the optional conflicts and circle any you are interested in.
3. Work through the rest of "Month Six." Every month will end with "Write What You Know" and a place where you can write down your new pitch. Try to finish your story by the 25th of each month.

Commit to the Lord whatever you do, and he will establish your plans. – Proverbs 16:3

THEME OF ATMOSPHERE

THEME: Atmosphere

SETTING: The climate goes from one kind to another. You decide if the climate goes from dry to humid, sunny to cloudy, hidden to revealed, calm to sudden disaster, non-habitable to habitable, or habitable to non-habitable, etc. Throughout the entire story, your character experiences a race against time.

3 HIGHLIGHTS (include): a wise person, a race against time, and something falls from the sky

WORD COUNT: 750-1,500

DEADLINE: 25th of the month

RESOURCES:

- *Giant Tales From the Misty Swamp,* Chapter 2: Climate Change
- *A Full Description of the Great Tornado in Chester County, PA* by Richard Darlington
- *The Hurricane Guide* by William Radcliff Birt
- *The Law of Storms* by John Ross
- *The Philosophy of Earthquakes, Natural and Religious* by William Stukeley
- *In the Days of Giants: A Book of Norse Tales* by Abbie Farwell Brown
- *Not to us, O Lord, not to us. But to your name give glory because of your lovingkindness, because of your truth.* – Psalm 115:1
- Other resources:

OPTIONAL CONFLICTS TO GET YOU STARTED

1. Your character tours the Qumran Caves during the winter where the Dead Sea Scrolls were found. He or she happens to find another scroll and wants to turn it in to the correct location. A thief is hot on the trail in the middle of a thunderstorm. You decide whether or not your character can reach the correct location before the scroll gets stolen or before it gets ruined in the rain. You decide if a wise person is at the safe location. Maybe a wise person journeys with your character or maybe your character is the wise person.

2. Your character lives in a secluded, desolate area called the Hanging Garden of Babylon where only ten secluded people can live. A wise teacher has taught your character how to read and write – and how to survive harsh conditions of regular derechos (fast-moving windstorms) far away from civilization. Trouble sets in when an eleventh person is added, due to a love relationship. Your character is chosen to leave or die. You decide if your character leaves or if your character makes the new person leave or some other ending.

3. Your character is a wise engineer who must save a historical monument from getting destroyed, perhaps it might be destroyed by a powerful time bomb or a group of rioters. A villain might be seeking revenge against an organization. You decide which monument is at risk. You decide which organization is being terrorized. You decide if a tornado wipes out the criminals or if a thunderstorm strikes one of the criminals. You decide if a flood, five tornadoes, or a firestorm stops the criminal from carrying out his criminal activity.

4. Your character is one of Noah's sons, his wife, or one of his three daughter-in-laws. A wise construction worker is named Noah. The town people make fun of Noah for thinking water is going to fall from the sky. Noah sees the waters springing up from deep in the ground, increasing in pressure, and he knows his time is running short. You must describe the terribly wicked nature of all the town people. You decide what your character does before the door shuts them in the ark.

5. Your character has been given a special gift to see visions into a spiritual world where Michael the wise archangel is leading a great army of warrior angels to fight against the Dragon and his fallen angels. Now that the US Embassy has been moved to the proper location, Michael asks your character to help get

the third temple rebuilt on the temple mount. You decide what your character will do to help get it rebuilt – before mass genocide wipes out half the population on earth.

6. Your character gets a new job and quickly learns that the atmosphere in the swamp is less than ideal. With a dominating boss who demands perfection, the staff acts corruptly in order to deal with it. One lies. Another one remains bottled up. Another one denies when other people do good. Another one sneaks alcohol in. On an unusually hot day, your character must find a way to build positive teamwork and recognize good accomplishments.

7. Your character speaks to a wise person who tells him the worst blizzard in history is going to hit their town. He must hurry and get to the store before the blizzard hits. While heading out to the store, four people get in his or her way. You decide if the four people include any of the following: an angry neighbor who does not like your character for some reason, another angry neighbor who is mad about the neighborhood rules, someone selling something, a car ran out of gas and is stuck in the road, a car wreck, a lost dog, or some other strange person. You decide if your character ever makes it to the store.

8. A dust storm suddenly hits a town for the first time ever in history. Cars stand still. People struggle to get inside shelter. No sunshine gets through. Your character is at a big old library where he or she speaks to a wise person about dust storms. One person in the library is worried about his or her teenager who was out walking the dog. You decide how your character saves the teenager. You describe the economic and cultural damage. When the dust finally settles and the sun comes back out, point out who is thankful.

9. The ground splits open and swallows three grumbling rebellious leaders and their grumbling families. A plague killed 14,700 grumbling rebels. Only non-grumblers are left. Your character might be the one who must select new leaders after the grumblers are gone. (Numbers 16-17)

10. Other conflicts you might want to write about: an ice storm, emergency communication, valleys split (Micah 1:40), ancient hills collapse (Hab. 3:4), an earthquake splits rocks (Mat. 27:51).

If any of you lacks wisdom, let him ask God, who gives generously to all without reproach, and it will be given him.– James 1:5

TOOLS FOR CREATING ATMOSPHERE

1. Sense Perception

   Become more aware of sense perception. Explore smells, tastes, sounds, and sights in order to see how they might freshen up your story in an explosive, tranquil, or surprising way.

   EXAMPLE: She finally welcomed the sound of the *squeaky* front door. Her mood changed when she opened the door and took in a deep breath of her mother's freshly baked *chocolate chip cookies*. The sight of the kitchen table and beautiful *center piece* comforted her once again. Her mother's *voice* melted away the pain she felt in her heart. For years, she had been too critical, and she knew it.

2. Better verbs and adjectives

   Carefully select strong verbs and vivid adjectives to bring development into focus a bit more without disrupting the flow of the sentence.

   a. EXERCISE: Select adjectives for the following story, "The Two Crabs," an Aesop Fable.

   One ______________ day, a _________________ crab ventured away from home to take a __________________ stroll on the sand. "__________ child," said the mother, "You shouldn't be walking sideways." "Yes, ___________ mother," said the crab. "But please show me how. I have only been walking the same way you do."

3. Personification

   Describe the setting using human terms. Identify an object or abstraction by giving it human qualities or abilities (falling in love, scratching his brain).

   EXAMPLES of personification: Time sure *runs* quick at the hobbit's desk. She had been ignoring the *sad* windows all winter. She walked to the *lonely* mailbox and found a treasure that changed her life forever. She stood in front of her house unaware of the silent, maple *arms* stretching wide open.

4. Topical terms - Make a list of terms from a category that fits with the genre, setting, conflict, or topic. Use the terms to create more vivid atmosphere.

FIGURES OF SPEECH – TOOLS FOR ATMSOPHERE

5. Analogies, similes, and metaphors - Compare your scene or objects in your scene to something else that would be familiar to the reader. Analogies, similes, and metaphors compare two things. A metaphor is saying something is something else, but it really isn't that something else.

EXAMPLES of a simile: …as fast as an arrow; the world is like a stage.

EXAMPLES of a metaphor: the world is a stage; her mind was on the moon

EXERCISE: Fill in the blank.

a. When she tried to move, it felt like ______________________.

b. His name was like a ______________________________.

c. Hearing the good news was like ____________________.

d. Life is like ___________________________.

e. Cup is to saucer as love is to ____________________.

6. Onomatopoeia – Use sound effect words such as boom, sizzle, cuckoo.

7. Pun – Use a witty play on words or names or even make up new words.

EXAMPLES: When the sun came up, she felt new as if nitrogen had become daytrogen. Her new middle name had become Energize.

8. Hyperbole – A writer can use hyperbole to emphasize a point, exaggerating for the purpose of giving a heightened effect.

EXAMPLE: The slimy salesman was talking to death.

9. Oxymoron – Using two terms that are incongruous or contradictory.

EXAMPLE: The pro-choice lady said she is for life.

10. Assonance – Using similar sounding vowels to make a point stand out.

WRITE WHAT YOU KNOW

What kind of struggle have you or someone else you know been through?

Where have you traveled recently?

1. DISCOVER A GOOD LESSON

What did you or someone else you know discover or learn during or after a struggle?

2. EXPERIENCE

What kind of experience did you or someone you know go through that you want to write about?

3. ANTAGONIST

What kind of antagonist do you want to write about?

4. APPOINTMENT

List a situation, meeting, or conversation you had recently that you could write about. Maybe it was someone else's conversation or a discussion you overheard.

5. HOOK

List several outcomes for a story conflict in order to identify your hook. You should hook your reader into wanting to find out what is going to happen.

6. WHAT IF...?

Think of a real situation or story, but then add drama by asking, *What if…?*

7. CONFLICTS

What other conflicts might occur in your story? What other conflicts stand out that you might want to write about?

8. ADDING DETAIL

What kind of topics, settings, or themes can you research to find terms that will add detail to your story?

Each month, we will build onto this list.

PITCHES & WRITING CONFERENCES

Please take a moment to write a one sentence summary for your short story. This is excellent practice and something you should get in the habit of doing.

A summary should tell three things:
1. WHO is the main character?
2. GOAL - what is the main character's goal?
3. OBSTACLE - what is the character's main obstacle?

Once you practice saying your pitch out loud, you can memorize it quite easily.

If you are going to make a 10-minute appointment with a publisher at a writing conference, then you ought to have a 5-minute pitch prepared ahead of time. Think about opening your appointment with something short and catchy. You could begin with describing your story as a mix between two well-known stories, but then you'll need to explain what you mean by that.

List any writing conferences coming up that you might want to attend:

1.

2.

3.

If you attended a conference, write down the names and contact information of editors and publishers. Make sure to follow up with them.

PITCH PAGE

Write a one sentence summary for each one of your stories.
These summaries can be for you to tell your family and friends. They can also be for you to tell agents, publishers, editors, readers, and reviewers.

MY PITCH FOR (TITLE, DATE)

---

1. Who is the main character?

2. What is the main character's goal?

3. What is the character's main obstacle?

MY PITCH

4. Write a longer pitch version for anyone who is interested in learning more about your story.

Print out your final draft. Write your pitch at the top of the page. Fold it in half. Place it here in this workbook. Repeat this process each month.

SEASON THREE TOPICS FOR MONTHS 7, 8, & 9

Month Seven: CARNIVALS

Month Eight: MASKS

Month Nine: HEIRLOOMS

Congratulations for making it this far! You are half way done. Welcome to season three.

OUTLINE FOR SEASON THREE: MONTHS 7, 8, & 9 TOPICS

I. MONTH 7: Carnivals

  A. Theme of Curiosity

  B. Mysteries

  C. Experts

  D. Write What You Know

  E. Pitches & Conferences

II. MONTH 8: Masks

  A. Theme of Disguises

  B. Feedback

  C. Write What You Know

  D. Pitches & Conferences

III. MONTH 9: Heirlooms

  A. Theme of Inheritance

  C. Write What You Know

  D. Pitches & Conferences

MONTH SEVEN TOPIC:

CARNIVALS

You have made it halfway! Good job! You should have at least six short stories so far. Stick with it. If at any time you want to write more than the word count range of 750-1,000, please do! You are in charge of writing more or less. Let your stories of life inspire you to write more. Welcome to *Month Seven!*

WHAT WILL WE DO IN THIS CHAPTER?

We will be covering the following items: optional conflicts, two kinds of *curious*, elements of a mystery, carnival adventure, experts, write what you know, and pitches.

DIRECTIONS: (Same each month)

1. On the next page, read the theme, setting, and three highlights.
2. Read through the optional conflicts and circle any that interest you.
3. Read through the next item, "Two Kinds of 'Curios'." Work through the rest of the chapter. Every month will end with "Write What You Know" and a place where you can write down your new pitch. Try to finish your story by the 25th of each month.

Whoever finds his life will lose it, and whoever loses his life for my sake will find it. – Matthew 10:39

THEME OF CURIOSITY

THEME: Curiosity

SETTING: At a carnival, street parade, circus, or a festival, your character finds a secret passageway and loses something. You decide what he or she loses. You decide what happens.

3 HIGHLIGHTS (include): A secret passageway, something lost, and an insect

WORD COUNT: 750-1,500

DEADLINE: 25th of the month

RESOURCES:

- *Giant Tales From the Misty Swamp*, Chapter 3: Carnivals
- *The Scarlet Letter* by Nathaniel Hawthorne
- *Under the Lilacs* by Louisa May Alcott
- *On the Road With a Circus* by William Carter Thompson
- *Circus Life and Circus Celebrities* by Thomas Frost
- *Theatrical and Circus Life* by John J. Jennings
- *Why, my soul, are you downcast? Why so disturbed within me? Put your hope in God, for I will yet praise him, my Savior and my God.* – Psalm 42:11
- Other resources:

OPTIONAL CONFLICTS TO GET YOU STARTED

1. After the Pinocchio show, your character becomes curious about Da Vinci's Flying Machine and loses track of his or her child. While the child is missing, you decide what happens. You decide the age of the child, where the child will be found, and why the child went missing.

2. At the carnival, your character enters a town library where he or she witnesses a carnival character who opens a revolving bookcase that leads to a secret passageway. You decide if your character finds a private wine cellar or a voyage to a new world. Leaving quickly, your character returns to the carnival only to find out he lost his keys. He must return to the bookcase and open it himself. You decide where he finds his keys and how he gets them back.

3. After the jousting event, your character finds a secret passageway and encounters a carnival witch. You decide how the conversation goes and if any agreement was made to part ways. After the conversation, your character has lost his memory. You decide how he or she gets it back.

4. Your character is tired of not being appreciated. Feeling worthless, he or she attends a carnival to find some fun. First, he witnesses someone who flaunts wealth while stealing. Second, he witnesses someone who shows off his strength. Third, he witnesses someone who fools others with fake magic tricks. Finally, he speaks with a humble carnival worker who finds value in finding ways to show acts of kindness. On the way home, your character looks up to see the many stars. He suddenly feels loved by His Creator and realizes that is all he needs to find his dignity.

5. At the carnival, your character enters into the Three Sisters Labyrinth. While roaming around and turning many corners, he encounters a statue of the immortal Sthenno. A few more corners later, he encounters another statue, the immortal Euryale. Reading the sign, it says that the third sister is mortal, Medusa. Not wanting to be in a labyrinth of Greek Mythology, your character panics and turns to leave. Later at the carnival, he discovers his phone is missing. Thinking he must have dropped it in the Three Sisters Labyrinth, he must return to find it. You decide if Medusa has it and whether your character ever gets his cell phone back.

6. Your character has a blast at the carnival. On the way out, he or she buys a carnival balloon from a carnival clown. Out in the parking lot, your character discovers his wallet is missing. Knowing he just bought a balloon, he returns to find the clown. Seeing the clown walking farther away from him, your character continues to follow him. Leading to a crowd that is waiting for the next tight rope walking show, the clown starts climbing a fabric staircase. He makes his way out on the rope. After the show, the clown gets on stilts, walking out to center stage. He begins juggling with three wallets. Your character notices his wallet! You decide how and when your character finally gets his wallet back. You decide if your character gets paid for letting the clown use his wallet as a prop.

7. Your character works at the carnival. All is well until the jewelry box ballerina loses the key to her box. Problem after problem, you decide if lightning made the ferris wheel get stuck. You decide why the pantomime really lost his voice. Despite it all, the show must go on.

8. Your character has a fear of clowns. Describe what happened to make him or her afraid of clowns. You decide why he or she must enter the Clown Maze. The maze consists of numerous clowns and clown memorabilia. Maybe your character wants to face the fear. You decide if your character finally loses the fear of clowns.

9. Other conflicts that might happen at a carnival: a ride where you temporarily lose your memory, a villain stole a man's prosthetic limb, a group of new mommies bring their babies in strollers – the babies love it there so much, they don't want to leave, a worker must help a person find his dentures or his glass eye, a person finds a gun and tries to avoid trouble at every turn.

TWO KINDS OF *CURIOUS*

The word *curiosity* can be used in at least two different ways.

1. When your character has curiosity, he or she has a strong desire, interest and inquisitiveness, to know or learn something. Your character might be curious to find out what kind of games will be at the carnival.

2. Curious things can be something peculiar, strange, or odd about something else. For example, your character might hear about a haunted house at the carnival where strange, spooky kind of things are happening. Your character might be curious to find out what kind of curious things are going on inside the house.

TWO KINDS OF *CURIOUS* IN YOUR STORY

EXERCISE: Select one of the optional conflicts to work with right now. Then answer the following questions.

1. Will my character be curious to know something? If so, what is it?

2. What kind of curious things are going on?

MY SETTING & ADDING DETAIL

EXERCISE: Select one of the optional conflicts to work with right now. Then answer the following questions.

What conflict did you select?

1. What kind of carnival will be in your story? Describe it.

2. What kind of games, events, or characters will be there?

3. What kind of trouble is beneath the surface of the setting?

MYSTERIES

The nature of a mystery is something that is difficult to explain or it might even be impossible to understand. At the very least, a mystery usually defies our normal understanding. A clue can often help solve a mystery. Underline any of the following mysteries that interest you.

EXAMPLES of mysteries include dark matter, black holes, identity of Jack the Ripper, location of Cleopatra's tomb, who killed JFK, whether a money pit exists on Oak Island, whether a land called Atlantis ever existed, and the location of the Ark of the Covenant.

Other mysteries that interest you:

PARADOX

A paradox is something that seems absurd or contradictory, but upon closer examination, an explanation does exist. A paradox often needs to be explained. Underline any of the following paradoxes that interest you.

EXAMPLES of paradoxes include the bootstrap time travel paradox, wormhole paradox, free will paradox, optical illusions, infinite number paradox, Zeno's paradox, Monty Hall problem, problem of evil, Sorites paradox, pleasure paradox, a catch-22, Peto's paradox, alien paradox, telescope paradox, the Gordian Knot, and a culturally tolerant paradox.

Other paradoxes that interest you:

EXERCISE: Select a problem, either a mystery or a paradox, that seems impossible to solve. How would you solve the problem?

As a writer, one challenge will be to find a conflict that can possibly inspire a *cause and effect* kind of story. A story is a series of events. This one thing happened because this other thing happened and so on. A story based on a mystery should have a story that is unfolded in such a way that builds curiosity for the reader to keep turning the pages. When your entire story is based on a mystery, the reader should begin with a perplexing situation and start to wonder certain things such as how did it get that way, why did it get that way, or who made it that way?

ELEMENTS OF A MYSTERY

- A mystery usually includes a hidden unknown, suspects, and clues.
- The hidden unknown could be a situation that is partly known or fully unknown. The partly known part could be difficult to understand.
- An inquisitive person wants to find out more. He wants to get answers. He wants to at least find clues that might help him solve the mystery.
- Something remains hidden, and someone wants to find it.
- An evaluation is usually done at some point. This can include gathering information and finding any possible clues, suspects, and/or motives.
- The story must move in the right direction. A process of elimination, trial and error, risking it all, or working late into the night can help point in the right direction.

BIBLICAL MYSTERIES

EXERCISE: Circle any of the following mysteries that you might want to write about or include in your story.

- Trinity
- Incarnation
- Immortality
- Afterlife, heaven, and hell
- Seven stars and lampstands
- Babylon
- Garden of Eden
- Behemoth, leviathan, and sea monsters
- Giants
- 900-years old people

MYSTERY EXERCISE

DIRECTIONS: Select one of the following mysteries. Then answer the questions.

- Moai statues of Easter Island – ancient massive megalith rock carvings
- Confederate Treasury – gold and silver worth millions disappeared
- Gobekli Tepe- ancient archaeological site of pillars, circles, and images on rock
- Sea People – ancient aggressive sea farers – possibly the Philistines
- Antikythera Mechanism – ancient Greek devise used for astrological purposes
- Oak Island Money Pit – people die when searching for ancient buried items
- The Voynich Manuscript – an unknown language, alien plants, and strangeness
- WOW Signal – a signal from the constellation Sagittarius
- The Real Identity of Benjamin Kyle
- Dancing Plague of 1518
- S.S. Ourang Medan
- Baghdad Battery

1. What situation is only half-known or a paradox?

2. How will your character find out more about this mystery or paradox?

3. What seems to be the obstacle getting in the way?

4. How will your character evaluate clues? Suspects? Motives?

5. Will your character use process of elimination, trial and error, risk it all, work late in the night, or some other method to move in the right direction?

CARNIVAL ADVENTURE

DIRECTIONS: Answer the following questions.

1. Have you ever been to a carnival, festival, state fair, or parade? If so, list as many as you can.

2. Focusing on each journey one at a time, what part of the experience you enjoy the most?

3. In an action adventure, the character might be pursuing something. List a few different things, objects or achievements, your character might pursue.

4. What kind of signature action can your character display during the adventure?

EXPERTS

Will your story include an expert? If so, what kind? What kind of expert stirs your interest? Select any expert you might want to include in your story.

KINDS OF EXPERTS

- Psychiatry – Adult, old age, child, learning disabilities, addictions
- Medical – Forensics, nurse, neurology, doctor, pharmacist
- Criminal expert - Human trafficking, kidnapping, thief
- Country – Apiculturist, agriculturist, veterinarian, biochemist
- Meteorologist, wildfire
- Food or chemicals – Chef, baker, restaurant manager, B&B
- Literary – Librarian, writer, editor, publisher, agent,
- Engineer – environmental, chemical, civil, electrical, mechanical
- Computers – App developer, programmer
- Architecture – Landscaper, retail, urban, restoration, lighting
- Design – Artist, industrial design, furniture, textile, graphic, photo
- Other:

KINDS OF MYSTERIES

Cozy Mysteries – An upright intelligent civilian is the protagonist who brilliantly solves a crime.

Odd Mysteries – This kind of mystery involves strange things that are happening. The protagonist is intelligent but not necessarily an expert at anything.

Scientific, Technical, Legal, or Forensic Mysteries – This kind of mystery involves knowledge in specific areas such as from the work of policemen, doctors, lawyers, or other technical experts.

WRITE WHAT YOU KNOW

What kind of struggle have you or someone else you know been through?

Where have you traveled recently?

1. DISCOVER A GOOD LESSON
What did you or someone else you know discover or learn during or after a struggle?

2. EXPERIENCE
What kind of experience did you or someone you know go through that you want to write about?

3. ANTAGONIST
What kind of antagonist do you want to write about?

4. APPOINTMENT
List a situation, appointment, or conversation you or someone else had recently that you could write about.

5. HOOK
List several outcomes for your story in order to identify your hook. You should *hook* your reader into wanting to find out what is going to happen.

6. WHAT IF…?

Write down a real situation you experienced, but then add drama by asking, *What if…?*

7. CONFLICTS

What other conflicts might occur in your story?

8. DETAILS

What kind of topics, settings, or themes do you need to research to add detail?

Each month, we will build onto this list.

PITCHES & WRITING CONFERENCES

Please take a moment to write a one sentence summary for your short story. This is excellent practice and something you should get in the habit of doing.

A summary should tell three things:
1. WHO is the main character?
2. GOAL - what is the main character's goal?
3. OBSTACLE - what is the character's main obstacle?

Once you practice saying your pitch out loud, you can memorize it quite easily.

If you are going to make a 10-minute appointment with a publisher at a writing conference, then you ought to have a 5-minute pitch prepared ahead of time. Think about opening your appointment with something short and catchy. You could begin with describing your story as a mix between two well-known stories, but then you'll need to explain what you mean by that.

List any writing conferences coming up that you might want to attend:

1.

2.

3.

List any editors or publishers you need to follow up with.

PITCH PAGE

Write a one sentence summary for each one of your stories.
These summaries can be for you to tell your family and friends. They can also be for you to tell agents, publishers, editors, readers, and reviewers.

MY PITCH FOR (TITLE, DATE)

---

1. Who is the main character?

2. What is the main character's goal?

3. What is the character's main obstacle?

MY PITCH

Commit to the Lord whatever you do, and he will establish your plans. – Proverbs 16:3

4. Write a longer pitch version for anyone who is interested in learning more about your story.

Print out your final draft. Write your pitch at the top of the page. Fold it in half. Place it here in this workbook. Repeat this process each month.

MONTH EIGHT TOPIC:

____

MASKS

You should have at least seven stories and pitches. Good job! Keep up the good work! Write the current month and year on the line above.

Welcome to *Month Eight!*

WHAT WILL WE DO IN THIS CHAPTER?

We will be covering the following items: optional conflicts, types of disguises, feedback, write what you know, and pitches.

DIRECTIONS: (Same each month)

1. On the next page, read the theme, setting, and three highlights.
2. Begin to think about what kind of story you would like to write.
3. Work through the rest of "Month Eight." Every month will end with "Write What You Know" and a place where you can write down your new pitch. Try to finish your story by the 25th of each month.

Enemies disguise themselves with their lips, but in their hearts they harbor deceit. - Proverbs 26:24

THEME OF DISGUISES

THEME: Disguises

SETTING: You decide if the protagonist has a disguise or if the antagonist is disguised. Someone's true identity is hidden partially or fully. You decide how the disguise affects the conflict. The disguise might even be the cause of an undesired effect.

3 HIGHLIGHTS (include): A disguise, an engraving, and a body of water (a lake, river, sea, or ocean).

WORD COUNT: 750-1,500

DEADLINE: 25th of the month

RESOURCES FOR YOU TO EXPLORE:

- *Giant Tales From the Misty Swamp*, Chapter 4: Masks
- *Famous Imposters* by Bram Stoker, author of *Dracula*
- Shakespeare's *As You Like It* and *A Midsummer Night's Dream*
- *An Unsocial Socialist* by Bernard Shaw
- *Adventures and Enthusiasms* by Edward Verrall Lucas
- *So that we may no longer be children, tossed to and fro by the waves and carried about by every wind of doctrine, by human cunning, by craftiness in deceitful schemes.* – Ephesians 4:14
- Other resources:

OPTIONAL CONFLICTS TO GET YOU STARTED

1. Your character has been working so long and hard to perform something on a certain day. You decide if it's a theatrical performance, a musical performance, an athletic performance, or some other kind of work performance, etc. Worried at first about how well it will go, the day happened to turn out better than normal. However, the next day, a false report came out, giving credit to someone else for the work your character did. You decide what your character is going to do about it, if anything at all.

2. Your character has been so kind, working and serving at your child's school. A teacher or another parent there turns against your character, accusing your character of gross misconduct, but your character has done nothing wrong. You decide what your character is going to do about it, if anything at all, and whether justice was served on its own.

3. Your character, Mr. Utterson, is friends with Dr. Jekyll. Utterson has crossed paths with the smaller, younger, pure evil disguise of Mr. Edward Hyde in order to see his terrible face, but Mr. Hyde always slips away. One day, Utterson visits Jekyll to offer his help in getting rid of Mr. Hyde, but Jekyll declines. Utterson finds out that Mr. Hyde is trying to kill Mr. Jekyll. For weeks, Utterson thinks that Mr. Hyde is gone for good, but when Dr. Hyde locks himself in his laboratory, Utterson and the butler find an ax to break the door down. You decide how the story proceeds. You decide how to write a new and better ending.
   (The strange case of Dr. Jekyll and Mr. Hyde was written by Robert Louis Stevenson and first published in 1886. It is now in the public domain, which means it is no longer under copyright. You are allowed to rewrite it.)

4. Your character meets someone at a graveyard and does not know it is a ghost. Visiting a loved one's gravestone during the day or at night, your character encounters a ghost who appears to look like a staff worker. You decide how your character figures out that the person is not a human being.

5. A friend invites your character to go on a double date. With high hopes, your character thinks he or she will be having a good time. When your character first meets the person on the date, all is well. The date seems sort of nice, quiet but nice. As the night goes on, the date becomes more unlikeable, edgy, and unpredictable. By the end of the night, the date has become scary and evil. You decide how your character gets away.

6. Your character lives as a prisoner who is chained in a cave with other prisoners. The masked prisoners can only see shadows on a tall wall to learn things. Behind them, a low stage wall sits where teachers hold up puppets or objects to teach lessons. The prisoners cannot directly see the state's teachers. Behind the teachers, a bright fire casts shadows of limited teachings on the tall cave wall. Finally, your character leaves the cave to experience sunshine of truth and real knowledge. He returns to the cave to become a teacher. Describe the journey. Inspired by *Pluto's Allegory of the Cave.*

7. An enemy tribe lurks out in the jungle or in a lab somewhere. Your character secretively places a totem pole gift for them to enjoy. You decide what the totem pole is really hiding; a microphone, camera, drone, chemical testing, etc. Thinking the totem pole is a sign to continue their evil plan, the enemy accepts it. You describe how your character gathers the information he or she needs to expose their evil deeds. Inspired by the story of the Trojan horse, you decide how the story ends.

8. A villain builds a gigantic underground bunker/city for the apparent thrill of unique living. Some people live there just in case living above ground is not an option. The villain seems nice, but he or she is really planning to take over the world. The bunker serves as a place where chosen people can actually live. One day, your character finds out about a plan to hold the world hostage. Needing to collect evidence of the villain carrying out this evil scheme, describe what your character must go through in order to save the world.

9. Satan and his fallen angels disguise themselves as angels of light in order to deceive and lead astray any human being who will listen to them (2 Corinthians 11:14-15). Your character has known someone for quite some time. You decide for how long. Somehow this person begins to lead your character astray. You decide how.

10. Other disguises you might want to write about: an angel, Shakespeare's Rosalind "Ganymede" from *As You Like It*, Puck from *A Midsummer Night's Dream*, angels talk to Abraham, a princess finds a frog, or an undercover detective.

TYPES OF DISGUISES

Disguises can vary from heroes to villains to other illusions.

SHOCKING DISGUISE OF TAMAR

One of the most shocking disguises we find in the Old Testament is the story of Tamar (Genesis 38). Judah had three sons, Er, Onan, and Shelah. Tamar's first husband, Er, died of wickedness before they had any children. Her deceased husband's brother, Onan, married her out of tradition. Onan secretively refused to have children with her by pretending to be trying to get her pregnant. He, too, died from his wickedness. Tamar's father-in-law, Judah, thought Tamar was a source of grief, and he began to exclude her, sending her back to live with her father. By tradition, Tamar was supposed to marry Shelah, but Judah refused to give Shelah in marriage to Tamar.

One day, determined to get pregnant from the family line of Judah, Tamar pretended to be a harlot. Not knowing the identity of the harlot, Judah had intimate relations with her in exchange for a (pet) animal. As a promise to return with the animal, Judah left behind his signet, bracelets, and staff. Judah left to get an animal, but when he returned, she was gone. When he asked about the harlot, no one knew anything about her. Three months later, Judah found out that Tamar had disguised herself as a harlot, and she was now three months pregnant. Judah thought what she did was righteous, but he did not marry her. Tamar gave birth to twins, Perez and Zarah. The legal seed of Jesus's father Joseph was carried down from Noah to Perez to King David's son Solomon to Joseph the father who adopted Jesus after a virgin birth (Matthew 1:1-17) whereas the genealogy of Mary differs. The royal holy seed that came to Mary traveled down from Noah to Perez to King David's son Nathan to Mary the mother of Jesus (Luke 3:23).

Other biblical disguises: Josiah in Megiddo (2 Chronicles 35:20-24), a donkey sees an angel (Numbers 22), three divine messengers appear as men to Abraham (Genesis 18), Rebekah disguises her younger son Jacob as his older twin, Esau, in order to gain a special blessing (Genesis 27), Satan disguises himself as an angel of light (2 Corinthians 11:14).

FAMOUS DISGUISE HEROES include the princess's frog, Clark Kent, beauty's beast, and a detective or journalist who pretends to be someone else in order to find clues.

STRANGE DISGUISE OF THE WOLF

In the European story of *Little Red Riding Hood*, we often wonder how the girl was fooled into thinking the wolf was ever her grandmother. The story warns us about dangers of the forest. Little Red should have obeyed her mother and stayed on the narrow path, but instead she picked flowers off the narrow path while the wolf snuck ahead of her to grandmother's house. Staying on the narrow path of righteousness is one key to a good life (Proverbs 4:26, Matthew 7:13-14, Luke 13:23-25).

DEVIL IN DISGUISE

A character who seems to be good may very well end up being the villain. Satan disguises himself as an angel of light, but their end will "correspond to their deeds" (2 Corinthians 11:12-15). In a murder mystery, several suspects are examined in order to find the murderer.

EVIL SPY

In a spy story, one person in the group might be a spy or a betrayer such as Judas.

EVIL BETRAYER

One person in a group might be a betrayer such as Judas. On the other hand, one person in the group might be seen as the evil rat who turned against the group, but it could be that the person really ends up being a hero who discovers everyone in that group is corrupt.

EXERCISE: Circle any disguises on the previous pages you might want to write about.

Protagonist disguise:

Antagonist disguise:

Other disguises you might want to research or write about:

FEEDBACK

EXERCISE: Ask someone for feedback. An *alpha reader* is the first person who reads your story for the first time. A *beta reader* is a person who reads your story – usually after someone else has checked it for content, copy editing, and proofreading. After you write your 3-minute story, ask an *alpha reader* to read it. Tell them you need to know what they like about it, what they don't like about it, etc. You can select any of your stories from this workbook.

After the *alpha reader* finishes reading your story, ask your *alpha reader* these questions and jot down their answers as if you were interviewing them.

DIRECTIONS: Write down ten people who you can read three of your pitches to.

Select one to begin with. Ask him or her to read one of the three stories.

My Story Title ____

1. Did you find any glaring issues when you read the story?
2. What did you like about the story?
3. What didn't you like about it?
4. Do you think this story is ready for publishing?

Write down their feedback below.

1.

2.

3.

4.

FEEDBACK ON MY STORIES & PITCHES

Find an alpha reader who is willing to listen to three of your story pitches. Tell your alpha reader you need to get some feedback on your pitches. Read three of your pitches to him or her and ask which one he or she likes the best. Ask this alpha reader to read the story to the pitch and give you some feedback. Copy this page as often as you want. Use one photocopy per alpha reader.

THREE OF MY PITCHES

Which one of these pitches is the most interesting? Do you like all of them?

1.

2.

3.

Select one title: ____

1. Did you find any glaring issues when you read the story?
2. What did you like about the story?
3. What didn't you like about it?
4. Do you think this story is ready for publishing?

1.

2.

3.

4.

WRITE WHAT YOU KNOW

What kind of struggle have you or someone else you know been through?

Where have you traveled recently?

1. DISCOVER A GOOD LESSON

What did you or someone else you know discover or learn during or after a struggle?

2. EXPERIENCE

What kind of experience did you or someone you know go through that you need to talk about?

3. ANTAGONIST

What kind of antagonist do you want to write about?

4. APPOINTMENT

List a stressful situation or conversation you had recently that you could write about.

5. HOOK

List several outcomes for your story in order to *hook* your reader into wanting to find out what is going to happen.

6. WHAT IF?

Write down a real situation you experienced, but then add drama by asking, *What if…?*

7. CONFLICTS

What other conflicts might occur in your story?

8. DETAILS

What kind of topics, themes, and settings do you need to research to add detail? What kind of society is in your story?

9. TWO KINDS OF *CURIOUS*

Will my character be curious to know something? If so, what is it?

What kind of curious things are going on?

10. MYSTERY

What remains hidden in your story?

11. EXPERTS

Will any experts be in your story? What kind?

Each month, we will build onto this list.

PITCHES & WRITING CONFERENCES

Please take a moment to write a one sentence summary for your short story. This is excellent practice and something you should get in the habit of doing.

A summary should tell three things:
1. WHO is the main character?
2. GOAL - what is the main character's goal?
3. OBSTACLE - what is the character's main obstacle?

Once you practice saying your pitch out loud, you can memorize it quite easily.

If you are going to make a 10-minute appointment with a publisher at a writing conference, then you ought to have a 5-minute pitch prepared ahead of time. Think about opening your appointment with something short and catchy. You could begin with describing your story as a mix between two well-known stories, but then you'll need to explain what you mean by that.

List any writing conferences coming up that you might want to attend:

1.

2.

3.

Who do you need to follow up with?

PITCH PAGE

Write a one sentence summary for each one of your stories.
These summaries can be for you to tell your family and friends. They can also be for you to tell agents, publishers, editors, readers, and reviewers.

MY PITCH FOR (TITLE, DATE)

---

1. Who is the main character?

2. What is the main character's goal?

3. What is the character's main obstacle?

MY PITCH

Commit to the Lord whatever you do, and he will establish your plans. – Proverbs 16:3

4. Write a longer pitch version for anyone who is interested in learning more about your story.

Print out your final draft. Write your pitch at the top of the page. Fold it in half. Place it here in this workbook. Repeat this process each month.

MONTH NINE TOPIC:

____

HEIRLOOMS

You are almost 75% done! Stick with it. Write the current month and year on the line above. Welcome to *Month Nine!*

WHAT WILL WE DO IN THIS CHAPTER?

We will be covering the following items: optional conflicts, theme of inheritance, strange ways to inherit wealth, write what you know, and pitches.

DIRECTIONS: (Same each month)

1. On the next page, read the theme, setting, and three highlights.
2. Read the optional conflicts and circle any that interest you.
3. Work through the rest of "Month Nine." Every month will end with "Write What You Know" and a place where you can write down your new pitch. Try to finish your story by the 25th of each month.

THEME OF INHERITANCE

THEME: Inheritance

SETTING: Select a particular place that is usually private or empty such as an attic, an abandoned location, a meeting room, conference room, or a room that people avoid. Your character inherits an heirloom in that location. You decide what he or she inherits. You decide what kind of conflict your character must face.

3 HIGHLIGHTS (include): a private place, a sketch (outline, drawing, or an engraving), and an heirloom that has been inherited

WORD COUNT: 750-1,500

DEADLINE: 25th of the month

RESOURCES FOR YOU TO EXPLORE:

- *The Tragedy of King Lear* by William Shakespeare
- *Sense and Sensibility* by Jane Austen
- *Our Mutual Friend* by Charles Dickens
- *Furniture of the Olden Time* by Frances Clary Morse
- *Across Asia on a Bicycle* by Thomas Gaskell Allen and William Lewis
- *We live with an inheritance that can never perish, spoil, or fade. This inheritance is kept in heaven for you.* 1 Peter 1:4

OPTIONAL CONFLICTS TO GET YOU STARTED

1. Your character inherited an old bike. He or she finally takes it to a pawn shop to find out how much it is worth. After he realizes the historical value, your character faces a conflict with a relative who wants it. Should your character sell it? Keep it? Is it a curse? A blessing? You decide if he builds a bike park.

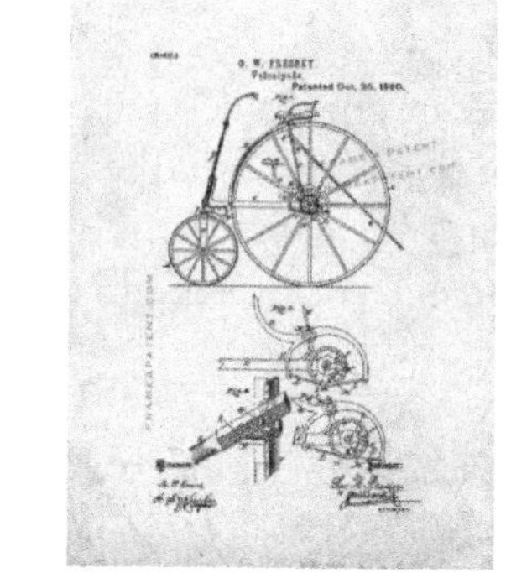

2. Your character inherits 100 million dollars from a long lost relative. Suddenly, he has many friends and family who love him. You decide what he does and how it changes his life.

3. Your character inherits 100 million dollars from a long lost relative, but there is one important rule if he takes it. He must travel to a specific deserted island and survive for one month. You decide whether he survives on the island and whether he gets the money.

4. Your character inherits a special divine painting. You decide what it is made out of and where it came from. The scene in the painting seems to be giving a message of some kind. You decide what kind of scene is painted on the canvas. You decide what kind of important message is given to your character. You decide how it affects your character and how your character responds. Inspired by Belshazzar's feast and writing on the wall in Daniel 5, you decide what kind of warning is given in the painting.

5. An elderly lady passed away living all alone. After doing some genealogy research, a villain discovers one living relative who lives far away. The villain pretends to be that living relative. The villain receives the inheritance. You decide how he gets caught or if he gets caught at all.

6. A woman was adopted and does not know her biological parents. She begins to search for her biological parents and finds out about their whereabouts. You decide how she finds them. She learns that only one is alive and gravely ill. She also learns that her biological parent is wealthy. You decide if she visits her parent before the parent dies and whether she gets the inheritance.

7. Your character privately inherited Moses's ark of the covenant (Exodus 25:10-22). At first, your character does not understand the history of it nor the rules for how to transport it. He quickly learns that he cannot touch it. He can only touch the poles. Should he hide it? Should he put it in a museum? Show the obstacles that get in the way every time he attempts to tell someone about it. You decide where it ends up.

8. Your character's parents die, leaving a will behind and three children. At the reading of the will, the children find out what they have inherited. You decide what your character inherits and how it affects the rest of the family. You decide if an evil relative might try to get the inheritance from the children (Example: Count Olaf from *A Series of Unfortunate Events*).

9. Other inheritances you might write about: An inheritance of a painting worth $400,000, a collection of baseball cards worth 3 million dollars, a collection of gold coins worth over 7 million dollars, a young man died and left his winery to his young son, a luxury railcar, model car collection, vintage dress collection, 50,000 records, 7,000 kinds of bones, a collection of 5,000 dolls, a collection of 200 reptiles, a model train set, a vintage car worth $600,000, a collection of 250,000 ancient arrowheads, or a grand piano owned by a famous piano player.

10. Your character inherits enough money to build a log cabin. Your character and a friend travel to a forest where they cut down trees in order to build a log cabin. While building the cabin with a team of people, they encounter an unusual creature. You decide how your character's friend dies. This turning point gives your character a reason to search for the elixir of immortality. Inspired by the ancient story of Gilgamesh, your character finds a divine seed believed to give eternal life, but after losing it, he finds out that the seed was taken back by the Guardian Angel of Eden. You decide how your character inherits a gift from the trinity of eternal life.

Blessed be the God and Father of our Lord Jesus Christ!
According to his great mercy, he has caused us to be born again to a living hope
through the resurrection of Jesus Christ from the dead,
to an inheritance that is imperishable, undefiled, and unfading,
kept in heaven for you, who by God's power are being guarded through faith
for a salvation ready to be revealed in the last time.
- 1 Peter 1:3-5

THINGS THAT PEOPLE INHERIT

The two most common things people inherit are flatware and furniture. We often think of people passing on a person's wealth, money, property, or business rights upon the death of another individual. However, many people end up passing on jewelry, photo albums, quilts, recipes, diaries, recipes, weapons, and clocks. While an inheritance is usually given after a person has passed away, it can also be given while they are alive. An inheritance can also be in the form of a promise made and a promise kept.

What are the two most common things people inherit?

___________________________ and ___________________________

Types of furniture include the following: chair, recliner, rocking chair, couch, bed, desk, game table, dining table, end table, poker table, cabinet, baker's rack, bookcase, gun cabinet, safe, chest, and wine rack.

EXERCISE: Circle any of the heirlooms above that you might want to include in your story.

COVENANTS

In the case of Abraham, news of his inheritance arrived in the form of at least seven promises. He died not receiving all of the promises in his lifetime, but he knew many of the promises would be fulfilled after his death, which we can find in historical records and see in the world today. A covenant promise was made by God to Abraham. Abraham was to receive the following:

1.) Abraham was made into a great nation where all nations would be blessed through him. He was blessed and became the *father of many nations and kings* (Gen. 12:2-3, Gen. 15:1, Gen. 17:4-6, 18:18, Gen. 25:1-4, 12-18, Gen. 36, Gen. 46, Gen. 49).
2.) Abraham and his descendants were to receive the *land* of Canaan forever (Gen. 13:14-17, Gen. 17:8)).
3.) Abraham would be the grandfather of *innumerable* descendants, as numerous as the stars - to all who believe (Gen. 15:5, Romans 4:11-16).
4.) At 100 years old, Abraham would become the father of Isaac. He would become the father of Jesus - through his son Isaac, through his son Jacob, through his son Judah - who would conquer all enemies (Gen. 21:5, Gen. 49:10).
5.) Abraham's *name would become great* (Gen. 12:2).
6.) Abram inherited *a new name*, Abraham (Gen. 17:5).
7.) Abraham inherited *righteousness* according to his faith (Romans 4:1-3).

RESEARCH ON ETERNAL LIFE

1. Where does a person inherit eternal life? From a potion? An elixir? A tree of life? A certain holy water from a holy fountain?

   A restored Garden of Eden will be restored with the river of life and the tree of life (Rev. 21:6-8, Rev. 22:1-5, 14). Is this literal or symbolic?

2. How is this eternal life received? (John 3:16)

   By believing in Jesus, the Son of God. Jesus said in John 3:16, "For God so loved the world - that He gave His one and only Son. Whosoever *believes in Him* shall not perish, but he shall inherit eternal life."

3. How can we find the fountain of life? (Proverbs 14:27, John 4:10, 7:38, 10:10).

4. What kind of eternal life can be inherited?

   Revelation 21 says the blessing of eternal life is in a resurrected body (Rev. 20:4-6).

5. Who gives eternal life?

   Does Jesus give eternal life? (John 3:36, 10:28-30, 1 John 5:11-13, Romans 6:23)

   Does the Holy Spirit give eternal life? (Gal. 6:8)

   Does God give eternal life? (2 Cor. 5:1)

STRANGE WAYS TO INHERIT WEALTH: a forgotten relative, a feisty friend, x-spouse, unknown twin, frequent customer, a random name, or giving birth via in vitro fertilization to someone with no children.

WRITE WHAT YOU KNOW

What kind of struggle have you or someone else you know been through?

Where have you traveled recently?

1. DISCOVER A GOOD LESSON
What did you or someone else you know discover or learn during or after a struggle?

2. EXPERIENCE
What kind of experience did you or someone you know go through that you want to write about?

3. ANTAGONIST
What kind of antagonist do you want to write about?

4. APPOINTMENT
List a stressful situation or conversation you had recently that you could write about.

5. HOOK
List several outcomes for your story in order to hook your reader into wanting to find out what is going to happen.

6. WHAT IF?
Write down a real situation you experienced, but then add drama by asking, *What if…?*

7. CONFLICTS
What other conflicts might occur in your story?

8. DETAILS
What kind of theme, setting, or topic do you need to research to add detail?
What kind of society is in your story?

9. TWO KINDS OF *CURIOUS*
Will my character be curious to know something? If so, what is it?

What kind of curious things are going on?

10. MYSTERY
What remains hidden in your story?

11. EXPERTS
Will any experts be in your story? If so, what kind?

Each month, we will build onto this list.

PITCHES & WRITING CONFERENCES

Please take a moment to write a one sentence summary for your short story. This is excellent practice and something you should get in the habit of doing.

A summary should tell three things:
1. WHO is the main character?
2. GOAL - what is the main character's goal?
3. OBSTACLE - what is the character's main obstacle?

Once you practice saying your pitch out loud, you can memorize it quite easily.

If you are going to make a 10-minute appointment with a publisher at a writing conference, then you ought to have a 5-minute pitch prepared ahead of time. Think about opening your appointment with something short and catchy. You could begin with describing your story as a mix between two well-known stories, but then you'll need to explain what you mean by that.

List any writing conferences coming up that you might want to attend:

1.

2.

3.

Who do you need to follow up with?

PITCH PAGE

Write a one sentence summary for each one of your stories.
These summaries can be for you to tell your family and friends. They can also be for you to tell agents, publishers, editors, readers, and reviewers.

MY PITCH FOR (TITLE, DATE)

1. Who is the main character?

2. What is the main character's goal?

3. What is the character's main obstacle?

MY PITCH

Commit to the Lord whatever you do, and he will establish your plans. – Proverbs 16:3

4. Write a longer pitch version for anyone who is interested in learning more about your story.

Print out your final draft. Write your pitch at the top of the page. Fold it in half. Place it here in this workbook. Repeat this process each month.

SEASON FOUR TOPICS FOR MONTHS 10, 11, & 12

Month Ten: TRICKSTERS

Month Eleven: NOISES

Month Twelve: EMERALD CITY

Congratulations for making it to the last season! Stick with it and finish strong!

OUTLINE FOR SEASON FOUR: MONTHS 10, 11, & 12 TOPICS

I. Month Ten Topic: Tricksters

  A. Optional Conflicts

  B. Nature of Tricksters

  C. Lovable Tricksters

  D. Write What You Know

  E. Pitches & Conferences

II. Month Eleven Topic: Noises

  A. Theme of Suspense

  B. Write What You Know

  C. Pitches & Conferences

III. Month Twelve Topic: Emerald City

  A. Theme of Compassion

  B. Write What You Know

  C. Pitches & Conferences

MONTH TEN TOPIC:

____

TRICKSTERS

You made it to the last season! Good job! Write the month and year on the line above. Welcome to *Month Ten!*

WHAT WILL WE DO IN THIS CHAPTER?

We will be covering the following items: optional conflicts, nature of tricksters, lovable tricksters, write what you know, and pitches.

DIRECTIONS: (Same each month)

1. On the next page, read the theme, setting, and three highlights.
2. Read through the optional conflicts and circle any that interest you.
3. Work through the rest of "Month Ten." Every month will end with "Write What You Know" and a place where you can write down your new pitch. Try to finish your story by the 25th of each month.

THEME OF DECEPTION

THEME: Deception

SETTING: Your character is being taken advantage of by a trickster who deceives people. At first, your character is fooled by delighting in a small bit of success, but the trickster returns with another offer. You decide if your character will fall for it a second time. You decide if your trickster is a quack psychologist, charlatan health care worker, gold digger con artist, business shyster, restaurant jester, neighborhood prankster, human trafficker coyote, property fraudster, or some other kind of trickster.

3 HIGHLIGHTS (include): A trickster, a trick, and a bell

WORD COUNT: 750-1,500

DEADLINE: 25th of the month

RESOURCES FOR YOU TO EXPLORE:

- *A Master of Deception* by Richard Marsh
- *Our Friend the Charlatan* by George Gissing
- *The Funny Side of Physic (The Mysteries of Medicine)* by Addison Darre Crabtre
- *Notes of a Gold Digger and Gold Diggers Guide* by James Bonwick
- *The Great American Fraud* by Samuel Hopkins Adams
- *The Flying Girl* by L. Frank Baum
- *The Magician's Own Book/The Whole Art of Conjuring* by George Arnold and Frank Cahill
- *Sketches of Imposture, Deception, and Credulity* by R. A. Davenport
- *Highways In Hiding* by George O. Smith
- *The Kingdom of the Cults* by Walter Martin
- Other resources:

OPTIONAL CONFLICTS TO GET YOU STARTED

1. Your character lives in a small town where everyone must vote on a property issue regarding the water tower. Since the water tower has a slow leak, it must be fixed. You decide if the mayor buys a brand-new tower from a trickster for $1 million. You decide how the leak began. You decide how three town people get involved. One wants to get a new tower. Another wants to fix the existing tower. Another has determined that the leak is harmless. You decide who the town sides with.

2. At a neighborhood BBQ, your character meets an outgoing shyster who seems trustworthy. The shyster says he can show your character how to make $200 a day, each day of the month. He invites your character to a private location where the shyster reveals a special printer that prints a new counterfeit $100 bill every 12 hours. Once your character pays $10,000 for this printer, he or she begins to collect several hundred-dollar bills. After three days, the printouts are blank. You decide how your character tracks down the shyster. You decide how the shyster gets caught.

3. Your character notices that one of his or her keychains is missing. It was a special keychain from a collection. Your character has collected quite a few keychains from places where he or she has vacationed. It was worth a lot of money. You decide what city it came from. The only suspects include the friendly neighbor boy who cuts the law, the nice cleaning lady, the responsible dog walker, or your character's own family member. Who is the trickster?

4. Your character is a wealthy person who does business with a lot of people. His or her spouse has gone missing. Never thinking it would ever happen, he receives a ransom note asking for $1 million in exchange for the spouse. You decide what happens.

5. Your character is a teenager with two younger siblings. His or her wealthy parents have died. You decide which long lost relative arrives to take care of them. After a series of unusual pranks from the relative, your character wonders if the relative is really related. Whether or not they are related, your character must try to find a new caretaker who they trust. Will they ever trust anyone?

6. Satan approaches your character as an Abbot and persuades him or her to become a monk. He quotes a verse from 1 Corinthians 5:11: *But now I am writing to you that you must not associate with anyone who claims to be a brother or sister but is sexually immoral or greedy, an idolater or slanderer, a drunkard or swindler. Do not even eat with such people.* Your character thinks that by becoming a monk, he will finally find peace and happiness. He begins living his new life at the Abbot's monastery with other monks only to find out they are operating a criminal network. You decide what kind of criminal activity is going on and how your character gets out.

7. A group of activists rise up in town to promote being peacemakers and tolerant of all people. During their seemingly innocent campaigns, your character notices that the leaders do not tolerate people who have moral boundaries. Your character must find a powerful way to show that the false peacemakers are breaking their own rules when they are intolerant of people who have moral boundaries.

8. Your character used to be the mayor of a certain town. The town attorney wrongly charged him or her with obstruction of justice. The county judge banished him to live out in the forest. He began to build tiny homes and sold many to people from faraway places. Gaining wealth out in the forest, his hometown begins to fear he will return with vengeance to rule over them. You decide if the real villain in town might be one of the following: the barber, banker, realtor, or landscaper.

9. A false prophet has risen in town, promoting "be whoever you want to be, as long as it aligns peacefully with human flourishing." This false prophet thinks he or she can accept people more than religious people. Not approving of religious dogma of any kind, he opposes the doctrines of sin, repentance, the trinity, and divine authority. Your character must stick together with a wise group that welcomes the Word of God. You describe the troubles they must endure.

10. Other tricksters you might want to write about: an election hacker, false healthcare worker, a scientist who falsely raises someone from the dead.

Beloved, do not believe every spirit, but test the spirits to see whether they are from God, for many false prophets have gone out into the world. - 1 John 4:1

NATURE OF TRICKSTERS

A trickster is one kind of a villain who uses deceit in order to manipulate someone else. They usually do not use violence to get what they want. Instead, they lie, cheat, or steal. They like to take advantage of vulnerable people or normal people who are in a vulnerable position.

CON ARTIST

A con artist is one kind of a trickster. He can be found in any setting where he or she can carry out his scheme. His hiddenness might be tucked away on the internet hacking into an account, taking someone's property or identity, or he could be out in the open with normal people, playing a friendly card game. A con artist usually does not know when to quit his foolishness. He might pile one lie on top of another lie in order to keep his manipulating game going, often taking on a new direction of deceit, until he gets caught. He might even change identities to hide a past identity or he might change identities to fool a certain kind of crowd.

You might find a con artist at any one of the following locations:

- Doctor or psychologist's office or on the internet
- Corporate conference room or at a friendly card game
- BBQ or neighborhood social
- Transportation stations such as the airport, train, or subway

EXERCISE: Have you ever been fooled? If so, write down what happened.

OTHER NAMES FOR A TRICKSTER

Swindler, fraudster, charlatan, quack, impostor, scoundrel, deceiver, joker, shyster, or con artist

LOVABLE TRICKSTERS

How lovable is a trickster? It varies from one to another. Some of the more lovable tricksters include Tinker Bell, Puck "Robin Goodfellow" the prankster from Shakespeare's *Midsummer Night's Dream*, the Cheshire Cat, Willy Wonka, Bugs Bunny, Eddie from *Leave It To Beaver*, Fred and George Weasley from Harry Potter, Captain Jack Sparrow, and Jacob who pretended to be his twin brother Esau, deceiving his own father, Isaac, in the book of *Genesis*. Other tricksters might have a more dramatic mixture of good and evil. Stanley from *The Mask* is an example of a normal person who becomes terribly mischievous, inspired by the classic ancient character, Loki from Norse Mythology. Mixed tricksters might start off as a terrible rascal, but somewhere deep down inside, they have a good side such as the Grinch. Yet other tricksters remain terrible and never change their ways such as the Joker and Satan.

LOVABLE TRICKSTERS – Pulling pranks or enjoying a bit of chaos from time to time, lovable tricksters do not wish to do physical harm to anyone. A loveable trickster might even be your protagonist who struggles against a major opposition of some kind.

MIXED TRICKSTERS – A mixed trickster has a deeper level of evil tugging in his or her life. This kind of trickster is usually the antagonist – sometimes charming, sometimes a bully. He uses his evil ways to hurt feelings, rob victims, ruin relationships, or live with a vindictive spirit. He might want to be good, but he isn't.

EVIL TRICKSTERS – This trickster does not care if he or she has to use violence to carry out his or her evil plan. He has an enormous amount of hate, revenge, or complete destruction driving his life. He is "full of himself," which means he is a narcissist. He does not want to be good. He wants to be bad all the time. He won't stop until he gets caught.

WRITE WHAT YOU KNOW

What kind of struggle have you or someone else you know been through?

Where have you traveled recently?

1. DISCOVER A GOOD LESSON
What did you or someone else you know discover or learn during or after a struggle?

2. EXPERIENCE
What kind of experience did you or someone you know go through that you need to talk about?

3. ANTAGONIST
What kind of antagonist, villain, or trickster do you want to write about?

4. APPOINTMENT
List a stressful situation or conversation you had recently that you could write about.

5. HOOK
List several outcomes for your story in order to hook your reader into wanting to find out what is going to happen.

6. WHAT IF?

Write down a real situation you experienced, but then add drama by asking, "What if"?

7. CONFLICTS

What other conflicts might occur in your story?

8. DETAILS

What kind of topics, themes, and settings do you need to research to add detail? What kind of society is in your story?

9. TWO KINDS OF *CURIOUS*

Will my character be curious to know something? If so, what is it?

What kind of curious things are going on?

10. MYSTERY

What remains hidden in your story?

11. EXPERTS

Will any experts be in your story? What kind?

PITCHES & WRITING CONFERENCES

Please take a moment to write a one sentence summary for your short story. This is excellent practice and something you should get in the habit of doing.

A summary should tell three things:
1. WHO is the main character?
2. GOAL - what is the main character's goal?
3. OBSTACLE - what is the character's main obstacle?

Once you practice saying your pitch out loud, you can memorize it quite easily.

If you are going to make a 10-minute appointment with a publisher at a writing conference, then you ought to have a 5-minute pitch prepared ahead of time. Think about opening your appointment with something short and catchy. You could begin with describing your story as a mix between two well-known stories, but then you'll need to explain what you mean by that.

List any writing conferences coming up that you might want to attend:

1.

2.

3.

Who do you need to follow up with?

PITCH PAGE

Write a one sentence summary for each one of your stories.
These summaries can be for you to tell your family and friends. They can also be for you to tell agents, publishers, editors, readers, and reviewers.

MY PITCH FOR (TITLE, DATE)

---

1. Who is the main character?

2. What is the main character's goal?

3. What is the character's main obstacle?

MY PITCH

Commit to the Lord whatever you do, and he will establish your plans. – Proverbs 16:3

4. Write a longer pitch version for anyone who is interested in learning more about your story.

Print out your final draft. Write your pitch at the top of the page. Fold it in half. Place it here in this workbook. Repeat this process each month.

MONTH ELEVEN TOPIC:

____

NOISES

I see a light at the end of the tunnel! We only have two months left to go! Write the current month and year on the line above. Welcome to *Month Eleven!*

WHAT WILL WE DO IN THIS CHAPTER?

We will be covering the following items: optional conflicts, nature of suspense, cliffhangers, pace and story map, noises at night, write what you know, and pitches.

DIRECTIONS: (Same each month)

1. On the next page, read the theme, setting, and three highlights.
2. Read optional conflicts and circle any that interest you.
3. Work through the rest of "Month Eleven." Every month will end with "Write What You Know" and a place where you can write down your new pitch. Try to finish your story by the 25th of each month.

THEME OF SUSPENSE

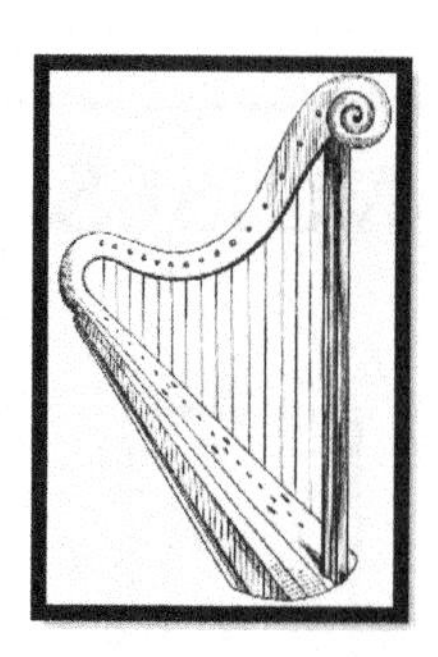

THEME: Suspense

SETTING: Suspense is building, and the stakes are high. Your character must hurry up before it is too late.

3 HIGHLIGHTS (include): a noise, something behind a closed door or a blocked pathway, uncertainty until the very end

THEME: Suspense

WORD COUNT: 750-1,500

DEADLINE: 25th of the month

RESOURCES FOR YOU TO EXPLORE:

- *The Hiding Place* by Corrie Ten Boom
- *Song of Hiawatha* by Henry Wadsworth Longfellow
- *Tremendous Trifles* by G. K. Chesterton
- *Of Ghosts and Spirits, Walking by Night* by Ludwig Lavater
- *Beasts and Super-Beasts* by Saki
- *Grimm's Fairy Tales* by Jacob Grimm and Wilhelm Grimm
- *Adventures in Silence* by Herbert W. Collingwood, a deaf author
- Other Resources:

OPTIONAL CONFLICTS TO GET YOU STARTED

1.) Blocked in a cave, your character survived when a cave collapsed. You decide if he or she was there as a visitor taking a tour or as an investigator. You decide why the cave collapsed – either a natural disaster or instigated by a villain. You decide how many people are stuck with your character in the cave. You decide what kind of noise they hear and what kind of trouble they face. You decide how long they must stay there until help arrives.

2.) Your character is a writer who is married to a curmudgeon. Over the years, he has become so cranky that it is almost unbearable to be with him in the same room anymore. He locks himself in a room called his Mancave. Your character wrote a book called *How to Stop Being a Curmudgeon*, but it only made things worse. You decide what he is doing in his Mancave all alone. You decide what kind of tinkering noises he is making. You decide why he is such a miserable person. You decide if he will ever come out of his Mancave alive.

3.) Your character is a construction worker who needs to work extra hours on a major construction project. Late into the night, your character is quietly working. Certain that everyone else has gone home, he or she hears a hammering, banging kind of noise far off in the distance. Feeling fearful, he ventures out to find what is causing the noise. Quietly approaching the noise, he finds an angry disgruntled employee who is ruining the construction project. You decide what happens. You decide if your character will survive throughout the night.

4. Your character bought a new house out in the country far away from anyone so that he or she can focus on writing his next bestselling book. After settling in, your character begins to… toss and turn at night when the rain is pouring and thunder is booming. Suddenly waking up to another particular sound on another night, he wonders what else could be so loud outside. He wakes up suddenly one rainy night and flashes his light out the window. Much to his surprise, he finds horses and chariots running wildly through his yard. You decide why the horses run by at night. You decide if a driver in a chariot stops to speak with your character. You decide if chariot races take place when lightning spooks the horses to run faster. You decide who might be running illegal horse races, gambling, and chariot races in the middle of the night. You decide if your character moves, joins the race, or finds a way to stop them altogether.

5. Your character has bought a new house out in the country far away from anyone so that he or she can focus on writing his next bestseller. After settling in, your character begins to… hear gunfire at night. Alarmed, he becomes worried, fearful, and angry. You decide who keeps shooting at night and why. You decide what your character is going to do about it. You decide if an hourglass can help solve the problem.

6. Out on a boat, your character is having fun with several other friends until dark clouds set in. Rain begins to pour and the sea begins to roar. The crew hears a particular machine noise like gears are grinding. What could it be? As their boat pounds over the waves, they discover Davy Jones and his ship are back from the dead. You decide if any of your character's friends survive.

7. Your character is taking a relaxing vacation on a cruise ship. Far away from land, an unexpected storm sets in. The captain has determined that the ship is going to sink. You decide what causes the ship to sink. Describe the panic that begins to stir up. Your character has an encounter with an angel who says that they must swim to an island close by. This story is inspired by Paul who was shipwrecked on the Island of Malta. Suspense builds in the middle of a storm out at sea until an angel gives Paul a message of hope (Acts 27:21-26). In verse 20, it says the people on board had given up all hope of being saved. Paul reassures them in verses 23-24.

8. Your character is part of a rescue team. A Jonah-type of man has secluded himself out in the forest, built a home, and has been trying his best to live apart from an unreasonable, uncivilized, sinful society. An earthquake hits, leaving his log cabin on the edge of a cliff. The man is stuck inside his cabin for three days. The entire story is about your character trying to rescue the man before his cabin falls down the side of the cliff.

9. Your character is a good scientist who is working hard to develop a vaccine to cure the world from a pandemic. Describe the financial offers and political rubbish he or she must face. Once the vaccine is ready, describe the trouble he or she faces in getting it distributed. You decide if a bad scientist gets in the way. You decide if your character's hometown will get the vaccine before the outbreak takes the life of his or her family and friends.

10. Other conflicts you might want to write about: Jonah tries to run away from preaching to a lost community, but a gigantic fish takes him there (Jonah 1-4).

Never be afraid to trust an unknown future to a known God. – Corrie Ten Boom, a Dutch watchmaker who helped many Jews escape the Nazi Holocaust during World War II.

SUSPENSE

Every good story has some kind of suspense to a certain extent. A reader wants to find a good hook that will keep him plugged in. The hook is a mild form of suspense. A good hook will give the reader the desire to know the outcome. What is going to happen? Is Little Red Riding Hood going to make it to grandmother's house? Will Captain Jack Sparrow get his Black Pearl back from Barbossa? Depending on the way the story is written, a certain level of anticipation can be achieved. Suspense becomes more dramatic when the reader is on the edge of his seat, wondering what is going to happen at any second. A good author learns how to withhold information until the very end.

DRAMATIC SUSPENSE

The word *suspense* means an uncertain expectation about what is going to happen next. In a moment of dramatic suspense, the reader wonders what is going to happen to the main character.

- *Will he get hurt?*
- *Will something bad happen to him?*
- *Will he find a way out? Will he survive?*
- *Will he get away from the bad guy?*
- *Will he make it out alive?*

Dramatic suspense differs from mild suspense in that dramatic suspense often gives the possible outcome of physical harm or even death. A mystery usually includes mild suspense where the reader wonders who killed so-in-so? *Will the main character find any clues? What will the main character do next?*

SUSPENSE DESTROYERS

An unexciting part of the story can ruin the pace of suspense. If an author is just trying to increase word count at the request of a publisher, it might be tempting to add scenes that do not really add to the story in any significant way.

Red Herrings - Another item that can destroy suspense is if the author includes irrelevant red herrings, obvious red herrings, or too many red herrings. If the reader thinks that one character might be a red herring, he might start to lose interest. If you decide to use a red herring, be very careful to not mislead or distract the reader from wanting to finish the story.

CLIFFHANGERS

At the end of the story, if the antagonist has not been completely stopped, the reader often is left to wonder if the story will continue in another story. In a cliffhanger, the main character has a conflict of some kind, but the ending leaves the reader to believe that the entire conflict has not been resolved. A good cliffhanger will resolve a large amount of conflict, but not all of it. A successful cliffhanger will give the reader enough satisfaction to believe that a big part of the conflict was resolved. An interesting cliffhanger will leave just enough of the conflict unresolved so that the reader will want to read part two to find out what will happen to the unresolved part.

CLIFFHANGER CHAPTER

At the end of a chapter, the reader can also wonder if something will get resolved. As an author, you will want to make sure you do not leave unresolved issues unless you have a purpose for it. A story with unresolved issues can be a real problem when the reader is left to believe the unresolved issue added no value to the story. For example, at the end of your chapter, your character was kidnapped. The reader will want to find out what will happen in the next chapter. In the next chapter, however, the character's dog was stolen. The reader will want to find out what happened to the dog, but if the missing dog is left unresolved, the reader will be left wondering how the dog was even a part of the story.

TYPES OF CLIFFHANGERS

- An unanswered question is the most common kind of cliffhanger.
- A loss is identified, either physical or emotional, a relationship, food, or shelter.
- A dangling carrot is something desperately wanted but out of reach.
- A glimmer of hope with a slim outlook, an almost impossible situation.
- A physical threat of someone in immediate danger.
- A ticking clock with a sense of urgency before a deadline.
- An accident with unknown consequences, unknown results.
- Unexpected news with possible trouble ahead.

EXERCISE: Circle any of the cliffhangers above that you might want to include in your story.

PACE

You are in charge of starting your story with a disturbance, then describe rising tension and let the story reach a climax, and wrap up with a good ending. In a classic story, the format will include three basic parts. In the first part, the reader discovers the conflict. In the second part, the reader discovers what the struggle looks like and how it is keeping the protagonist from achieving his goal all the way up to the climax of the story. In the third part, the reader discovers a final resolution.

STORY MAP

While some writers like to use a story map while other writers do not, a story map offers a lot of advantages for the writer to keep moving at a good pace and not get off track. A classic story map will have three main parts: the conflict, rising tension leading up to a climax, and a resolution. In addition to having three main parts, a story can also include turning points. A turning point is when something happens to add tension in the story. In theater, a classic theatrical show can include three acts where two or three turning points add drama to the plot. A story map can keep the big picture in view and help the author move forward all the way to the very end.

EXERCISE:
Select one of the conflicts to work with right now. Then use it to fill in the "storymap" diagram below.

Hook – Conflict – Rising Action – Obstacles – Climax – Falling Action – Ending
(Turning Point) (What is at stake?) (Sense of Urgency) (Resolution)

RESOLUTION

In a tragedy, the reader is left unhappy with the ending, but the story might teach a warning. If this evil happens in the story and nothing is done about it, then it can bring about a tragic ending. A story with a good ending will include a great resolution. Did the reader see good win in the end? Was the conflict resolved? Nothing is worse than leaving a reader with a non sequitur. A non sequitur is when a conclusion did not properly follow from the previous premises.

NOISES

Noises can add suspense to the story at just the right time. A ticking clock might remind the reader that the character better hurry up and get something done before something bad happens. A countdown can also remind the reader that the character is in a race against time before he permanently loses something. As an author, you can use a certain noise throughout the story to signify the need for conquering the dilemma. Perhaps a clocktower reminds the town people to do something.

NOISES AT NIGHT

One of the easiest ways to add suspense is to introduce a noise at night. The character might not know what is causing the noise. It could be a clink or a bang or a whistle. It might be an unusual sound up in a tree. It could be a sound of music or a sound of irregularities. It might even be a sound pattern of morse code. Sound is one of our sense perceptions that can add interest to the story. An unknown sound at night leaves the reader to wonder what is making the sound. A mysterious sound at night behind a closed door adds tension as to whether the sound is coming from something destructive.

- A knock at the door
- Footsteps
- Creaky door
- TV suddenly turns on
- Cupboard shuts
- Window opens
- Singing or humming
- Radio static with certain sounds in it
- Snapping twigs

EXERCISE

Select one of the sounds above to work with right now. Your character wakes up at night and hears this sound. List several things below that could be causing the noise.

Possible causes:

WRITE WHAT YOU KNOW

What kind of struggle have you or someone else you know been through?

Where have you traveled recently?

1. DISCOVER A GOOD LESSON
What did you or someone else you know discover or learn during or after a struggle?

2. EXPERIENCE
What kind of experience did you or someone you know go through that you need to talk about?

3. ANTAGONIST
What kind of antagonist, villain, or trickster do you want to write about?

4. APPOINTMENT
List a stressful situation or conversation you or someone else had recently that you could write about.

5. HOOK
List several outcomes for your story in order to hook your reader into wanting to find out what is going to happen.

6. WHAT IF?
Write down a real situation you experienced, but then add drama by asking, "What if…?"

7. CONFLICTS
What other conflicts might occur in your story?

8. DETAILS
What kind of topics, themes, and settings do you need to research to add detail? What kind of society is in your story?

9. TWO KINDS OF *CURIOUS*
Will my character be curious to know something? If so, what is it?

What kind of curious things are going on?

10. MYSTERY
What remains hidden in your story?

11. EXPERTS
Will any experts be in your story? What kind?

12. NOISES
What kind of noises can add suspense?

PITCHES & WRITING CONFERENCES

Please take a moment to write a one sentence summary for your short story. This is excellent practice and something you should get in the habit of doing.

A summary should tell three things:
1. WHO is the main character?
2. GOAL - what is the main character's goal?
3. OBSTACLE - what is the character's main obstacle?

Once you practice saying your pitch out loud, you can memorize it quite easily.

If you are going to make a 10-minute appointment with a publisher at a writing conference, then you ought to have a 5-minute pitch prepared ahead of time. Think about opening your appointment with something short and catchy. You could begin with describing your story as a mix between two well-known stories, but then you'll need to explain what you mean by that.

List any writing conferences coming up that you might want to attend:

1.

2.

3.

Who do you need to follow up with?

PITCH PAGE

Write a one sentence summary for each one of your stories.
These summaries can be for you to tell your family and friends. They can also be for you to tell agents, publishers, editors, readers, and reviewers.

MY PITCH FOR (TITLE, DATE)

---

1. Who is the main character?

2. What is the main character's goal?

3. What is the character's main obstacle?

MY PITCH

Commit to the Lord whatever you do, and he will establish your plans. – Proverbs 16:3

4. Write a longer pitch version for anyone who is interested in learning more about your story.

Print out your final draft. Write your pitch at the top of the page. Fold it in half. Place it here in this workbook.

MONTH TWELVE TOPIC:

____

EMERALD CITY

This is our last month. We are almost finished. What are we waiting for? Let's get this done! Write the current month and year on the line above.

Welcome to *Month Twelve!*

WHAT WILL WE DO IN THIS CHAPTER?

We will be covering the following items: optional conflicts, theme of compassion, Dorothy's three friends, write what you know, and pitches.

DIRECTIONS: (Same each month)

1. On the next page, read the theme, setting, and three highlights.
2. Begin to think about what kind of story you would like to write.
3. Work through the rest of "Month Twelve." Finish with "Write What You Know" and your new pitch. Try to complete your story by the 25th of each month.

THEME OF COMPASSION

THEME: Compassion

SETTING: An "Oz" type setting, the Emerald City, either figurative or literal. This means that your setting is a place where your character (a Dorothy type) is helping one, two, or three friends who each need something: bravery, brains, or a heart to love.

3 HIGHLIGHTS (include): Emerald City, facing a fear, and showing compassion

WORD COUNT: 750-1,500

DEADLINE: 25th of the month

RESOURCE FOR YOU TO EXPLORE:

- *The Wonderful Wizard of Oz* written by author L. Frank Baum

OPTIONAL CONFLICTS TO GET YOU STARTED

1.) Your character is a psychologist who has compassion on three clients with real fears. One fears walking alone at night. One fears losing electricity. One fears having no one to love him. You decide how your character will help each one to conquer his or her fear. You decide what kind of task the psychologist gives each one of the clients to accomplish. You decide if they are able to get it done. You decide if the task helped or not. You decide if the psychologist's faith and compassion played a role and to what degree. *Now faith is the assurance of things hoped for, the conviction of things not seen.* – Hebrews 11:1

2.) Your character is a compassionate community leader who was asked by the governor to share his or her heart at a conference designed to lift one another up during a crisis. The governor has found several speakers to speak on the issue of caring for humanity. Speaking at a location where many people will be present, your character is asked to speak on *Encouragement During a Pandemic.* You decide how your character will encourage the people to be brave, smart, and loving.

3.) Your character is a famous author who was asked by the president to write a book about unity. Your character accepts the challenge. He or she begins to interview people and ask them questions. He finds out that some people find unity in rioting and corruption. Others are afraid of rioting and corruption. They do not seem to care about making an effort to love one another or even to get to know their neighbors. You decide how your character's book helps his society become more compassionate. You decide the title of the book.

4. Your character gets a new job and moves to a town where an immoral, charming governor is leading the people into living lives of fear and immorality. Your character feels compassion for the town people. He finds three people who he can help in one day. He helps a fearful person, a hopeless person, and an apathetic person. Becoming a new team, you decide how the four of them lead the town into a better way of living. You decide if the governor ever has a change of heart.

5. Your character works as a florist and delivers flowers. He or she delivers birthday flowers to three different people in one day who are in the middle of a crisis. One has a bad marriage without any hope it will ever get better. One has no job, preoccupied with confusion and doubt. One has been stuck in worry, unable to love other people. They all vent on your character, then apologize. You decide how your character has compassion and how a little faith can move mountains (Matthew 17:20).

6. Satan has come in disguise as a politician, fooling millions into thinking he offers peace. He makes a new law stating that everyone has to be loyal to peace or be labeled as a rebel. As a sign of unity, he says everyone has to take a mark on his hand or forehead to show loyalty to peace and unity (Revelation 13:16-18). Your character becomes a rebel castaway on a prison island with other rebels. Having compassion on the large amount of "loyal" people, you decide how your character and three castaways expose the evil nature of this politician. You decide how the misinformed "loyal" people wake up from this politician's disguise.

7. Your character has remained single for a long time due to a tragedy that took place. Many years ago, he or she was dating someone and fell in love. One day when arriving at the house, your character parked across the street. Delighted to see your character, this person began to run out and greet your character with a big hug. Not seeing a truck speeding down the street, your character witnessed his or her lover get hit by the truck. Many years later, your character must help three people in order to conquer a cold heart, fear, and uncertainty.

8. Your independent character has lost his or her job. One night in a dream, he or she is given the task of helping three people or else a new job will never arrive. Upon waking, denial sets in. Avoiding the dream, interviews fail one after another. Opportunities arise to help others, but your character dismisses them all. The dream returns, and this time your character is ready to take it seriously. You decide what kind of three people your character must help.

9. Your character is losing patience with homeless people who do not want to make any changes. Describe how he or she will help three homeless people.

10. Other conflicts you might want to write about: a heart of stone (Ezekiel 36:22-32), the Good Samaritan Parable (Luke 10:25-27), Jesus had compassion on the crowd and multiplied food to feed them (Matthew 15:32-39).

The wicked flee when no one pursues, but the righteous are bold as a lion. Proverbs 28:1

NATURE OF COMPASSION

When a victim has a problem, it takes a bold hero with compassion to help make things better. For some people who live with a problem, the problem will continue unless some kind of compassionate intervention is made. Some people who live in captivity will remain in captivity until someone frees them.

EXAMPLES of demonstrating compassion:

- Giving basic needs of food, shelter, and clothing
- Providing safety from danger, medical help or security help
- Offering a sense of belonging, leading a group or club
- Showing appreciation for one another, pointing it out, giving recognition
- Helping others see the meaning of life, value life, understand reality
- Helping others use organizational skills, see beauty in life
- Helping others take steps to live out having a servant's heart

EXERCISE: Using the list above, write down three ways you have shown compassion on someone else or three ways you would like your character to show compassion.

1.

2.

3.

DORTHY'S THREE FRIENDS

EXERCISE: Describe the problem that Dorothy and her three friends had. How did their problems get resolved?

Scarecrow –

Lion –

Tin Man –

Dorothy –

WRITE WHAT YOU KNOW

What kind of struggle have you or someone else you know been through?

Where have you traveled recently?

1. DISCOVER A GOOD LESSON
What did you or someone else you know discover or learn during or after a struggle?

2. EXPERIENCE
What kind of experience did you or someone you know go through that you want to write about?

3. ANTAGONIST
What kind of antagonist, villain, or trickster do you want to write about?

4. APPOINTMENT
List an appointment, meeting, situation, or conversation you or someone else had recently that you could write about.

5. HOOK
List several outcomes for your story in order to hook your reader into wanting to find out what is going to happen.

6. WHAT IF…?
Write down a real situation you experienced, but then add drama by asking, "*What if…?*"

7. CONFLICTS
What other conflicts might occur in your story?

8. DETAILS
What kind of topics, themes, and settings do you need to research to add detail? What kind of society is in your story?

9. TWO KINDS OF *CURIOUS*
Will my character be curious to know something? If so, what is it?

What kind of curious things are going on?

10. MYSTERY
What remains hidden in your story?

11. EXPERTS
Will any experts be in your story? If so, what kind?

12. NOISES
What kind of noise will add suspense?

PITCHES & WRITING CONFERENCES

Please take a moment to write a one sentence summary for your short story. This is excellent practice and something you should get in the habit of doing.

A summary should tell three things:
1. WHO is the main character?
2. GOAL - what is the main character's goal?
3. OBSTACLE - what is the character's main obstacle?

Once you practice saying your pitch out loud, you can memorize it quite easily.

If you are going to make a 10-minute appointment with a publisher at a writing conference, then you ought to have a 5-minute pitch prepared ahead of time. Think about opening your appointment with something short and catchy. You could begin with describing your story as a mix between two well-known stories, but then you'll need to explain what you mean by that.

List any writing conferences coming up that you might want to attend:

1.

2.

3.

Who do you need to follow up with?

Congratulations on finishing this workbook! I hope you have at least twelve stories fastened in here with pitches you can share. I hope your stories will touch people's hearts, offer hope to those who are lost, and help make this world a better place.

We are destroying speculations and every lofty thing raised up against the knowledge of God, and we are taking every thought captive to the obedience of Christ. – 2 Corinthians 10:5

PITCH PAGE

Write a one sentence summary for each one of your stories.
These summaries can be for you to tell your family and friends. They can also be for you to tell agents, publishers, editors, readers, and reviewers.

MY PITCH FOR (TITLE, DATE)

---

1. Who is the main character?

2. What is the main character's goal?

3. What is the character's main obstacle?

MY PITCH

Commit to the Lord whatever you do, and he will establish your plans. – Proverbs 16:3

4. Write a longer pitch version for anyone who is interested in learning more about your story.

Print out your final draft. Write your pitch at the top of the page. Fold it in half. Place it here in this workbook.

For more information
please visit:

Writers750Program.com

(formerly writers750.com)

Made in the USA
Columbia, SC
23 April 2022